Bird

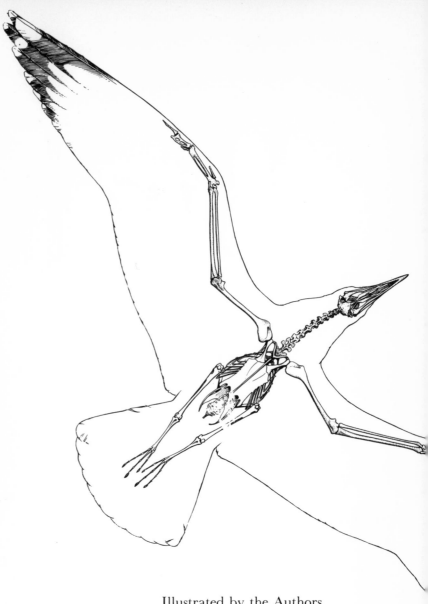

Illustrated by the Authors

Bird

Lois and Louis Darling

with a foreword
by Roger Tory Peterson

Houghton Mifflin Company Boston
The Riverside Press Cambridge

In memory of
Dr. James H. McGregor
teacher, scientist, artist, friend

Acknowledgments

DURING the long years in which this book has evolved we have received help from many people. Dr. Dean Amadon, Chairman of the Department of Ornithology, the American Museum of Natural History, read the entire manuscript and we are grateful for his helpful criticisms and suggestions. Dr. Bobb Schaeffer, Curator in the Department of Vertebrate Paleontology at the American Museum of Natural History and Professor of Zoology at Columbia University, repeatedly checked both text and drawings and contributed many basic ideas concerning presentation of the material.

We also want to thank our many friends of the Westport Audubon Society for all sorts of assistance. Edward and Barbara Beddall, Mortimer and Eloise Brown, Helen Leaycraft, and Milton Schwartz were especially generous in lending books, journals, and material and in helping us to evaluate the text and illustrations. However, as we have not invariably followed all advice, none of the above can be considered responsible for the contents of *Bird*.

LOIS AND LOUIS DARLING

Foreword

THE PLANETS spin through space, following their elliptical course around the sun. Most of them are eternally sterile but our own planet, small by astronomical standards, swarms with life. Many hundreds of thousands of living species, from 90-foot whales to minute protozoa, have been described by systematists and perhaps an even greater number of unknowns still await their inquiry. Practically all the birds have been catalogued by now, but it is actually still possible to find new avian species in obscure corners of the world.

According to the careful estimate of Ernst Mayr there are approximately 8600 species of birds in the world. The number of named insects must now exceed 860,000 (a third of which are beetles), and entomologists are still describing new ones at the rate of 10,000 species a year. So, then, for every bird species there are at least 100 species of known insects. Yet, conversely, for every entomologist there seem to be dozens of ornithologists — or bird watchers, or birders (call them what you will).

Statisticians have tried to estimate the number of bird watchers in the United States. Roger Barton pegged his guess at close to 10,000,000, an estimate based partly on readership of his weekly bird column for the Newark *Sunday News*. By taking a conservative 22 per cent interest factor and applying it to the 45,000,000 readers of all the nation's Sunday newspapers he arrived at his figure.

I suppose it depends on one's definition of "bird watcher." Certainly those who supply seeds for the chickadees and cardinals at the kitchen window or who take at least a casual interest in the birds they see must number millions. But if we take a more restrictive view and narrow things down to the "birders" — people who have invested in my *Field Guides* or the *Audubon Bird Guides* or some other bird book — the number must still exceed 1,000,000.

Identification is the first phase of interest of the serious birder. While his hobby is new, birds are added to his "life list" every time he goes out. But after three or four years, if he has been at all active, the life birds come slowly; they are spaced farther and farther apart. He may compensate for this by traveling to Florida for Limpkins and Everglade Kites; to Rockport, Texas, for a real migration binge; or to the Arizona desert for a whole new avifauna. But if listing is his only goal, his interest is bound to taper off unless he makes the transition to a broader interest in bird study.

The self-trained amateur may attend lectures at his natural history society. He may read voraciously or even subscribe to the more technical ornithological journals such as the *Auk*, the *Wilson Bulletin*, or the *Condor*. He will eventually know a good deal about birds, but his knowledge is likely to be spotty. A student in any university ornithology course may come off better; his regimen is planned for him.

Ever since I served in the Corps of Engineers of the United States Army, illustrating field manuals with numerous draw-

ings and schematic diagrams, I have entertained the fond
hope that someday I might apply a similar pictorial presentation to a book on the biology and attributes of birds, a book
for the layman. Therefore it was with keen interest that I
examined the first draft of this work submitted to my pub-
lisher, Houghton Mifflin, by Lois and Louis Darling. This
husband and wife team has co-authored and co-illustrated a
number of other books dealing with the biological sciences.

Louis Darling, an artist with a background and training
similar to my own, uses his draftsmanship as a teaching
medium. Both of us draw representationally, often decora-
tively. Neither of us (publicly, at least) goes in for "sub-
conscious comment," nor do we explore avant-garde tech-
niques. We draw for the purpose of explaining. The old
saw that "a picture is worth 10,000 words" may sound trite,
but in describing the shapes of things words can seldom be
as precise as accurate drawings. Even ideas can often be
better expressed visually. Lois Darling, who supplements
her husband perfectly in this joint endeavor, was formerly
a staff artist in the Department of Paleontology at the American Museum of Natural History. She furnished most of the
anatomical drawings as well as many of the others.

This book, with its numerous drawings, is designed to give
the lay reader some idea of what a bird is, what makes it
tick. It starts with the evolutionary history of the world and
then focuses briefly on the history of birds. The road between *Archaeopteryx*, the first known fossil bird, and modern
birds is paved with genesis and extinction and covers a span
of 150,000,000 years. The 8600 species of birds alive today
are but a tiny fraction of all the species that *have* lived — exactly what percentage we don't know. Recently two authorities, using their slide rules, came up with two quite different

answers: one contended that perhaps 250,000 species have arisen, had their day (actually, many thousands of years) and then slipped into the void of extinction; the other put the number of species at perhaps 1,500,000.

Bird psychology, one of the newest of the ornithological disciplines is discussed under the headings of instinct, display, and learning. Not so long ago writers often interpreted bird actions in the light of our own, as though birds were really little human beings clothed in feathers. The pendulum then swung from anthropomorphism to the mechanistic view that birds actually are automatons whose every reaction theoretically can be predicted. Only recently have some behaviorists admitted that birds do have individuality and that although most of their responses are automatic some birds, within limits, can meet new situations and learn.

The chapters on social behavior, migration, and flight cover some of the most exciting aspects of bird life. Birds have wings and they make incredible journeys. These facts more than any others account for their universal appeal. The items published about migrating birds are beyond counting. We know a lot of the details and minutiae about where they go and when, but we are only beginning to understand bird navigation. Indeed, just beginning.

The advanced amateur is almost certain to have read a good deal about migration and social behavior. His blind spots are more likely to be anatomy and physiology. Here, I think, the Darlings' book makes its most outstanding contribution. Nearly half of its pages are devoted to feathers, bone and muscle, digestion, circulation, breathing, the brain, the eye, the ear, and so forth. I, for one, will now have a clearer picture of how these organs function and how they enable a bird to live its very specialized and demanding life.

In a sense this book is not a treatise solely about birds. It is about life as illustrated by the birds. The reader is made aware of this in the epilogue — "Bird and Man." Those of us who watch birds have sometimes been accused of escapism, but if it be escape, it is from the unreal things, the synthetic, an escape from Megalopolis. The intelligent naturalist is more likely to know what makes the world go round than his biologically illiterate neighbors.

ROGER TORY PETERSON

Preface

OUR AIM in writing this book has been to provide a basic, simplified but scientifically valid account of the evolution, behavior, anatomy, and physiology of birds as well as a comparison of these features with those of other animals. We have tried to deal with the aspects of the bird important to the understanding of the broad principles behind the study of any form of life — the essence of bird life in the context of all other life.

We have not attempted anything like a definitive text on the biology of birds, a task next to impossible within the limits of one book. Nor do we talk about the wonder of some of the more "amazing" adaptations to life found in certain birds. This wonder is implicit in life itself, and we stand in awe of it from the simplest microorganism to man.

The ideal way to write a book of this sort would be to mention every aspect of the subject all at once. There is no first or most important thing about a living organism. Any life is the sum of a multitude of inseparable parts and happenings. Any living thing is interrelated with and dependent upon all other living things and upon the environment. To know any one part of this world of life requires some knowledge of all the others. Obviously it is impossible to describe everything first. The process of taking an animal apart and examining the pieces one by one, as we eventually must, is destructive to the very idea we are trying to express. So, rather unconventionally, we have left detailed consideration of anatomy, physiology, and of flight until the end. Actually the last eleven chapters could be read first. Their posterior position allows the reader to make his own choice to read them, first, last, in the middle, or a bit at a time; he can take them or leave them entirely alone. However, a good working knowledge of the information they contain will add immensely to the sum of one's appreciation and understanding of birds. Whichever procedure the reader chooses, he can help himself a good deal if he never lets these details stand in the way of a clear perception of the whole.

Bird is aimed at and dedicated to anyone, young or old, interested in living things. Birds, of course, are such beautiful and entrancing subjects that knowledge of them is an end in itself. But anyone who wants to go on from the identification of species can also find, through birds, a rich laboratory in dooryards, fields, woods, and even in city streets in which to search for a bit of the answer to those two great human questions, *how* and *why*. To express this idea more fully we shall quote the beginning lines in the introduction to one of the latest and best college biology texts, *Life* by George G. Simpson, Colin S. Pittendrigh, and Lewis H. Tiffany.

You are alive. That is the most important fact in the world. All around you are other living things. That fact is also important. It is, indeed, an aspect of the same fact. You would not yourself be alive if you were not a part of the whole complex world of life. This is true not only in the sense that you depend on other forms of life for food, but also in other and larger senses. You live in a community, a community of other humans and also of many other living things in greater diversity and of greater impact on your own life than you may have realized as yet. You share with them many processes of living. The study of these processes in other animals and in plants is necessary for an understanding of your own life. Moreover, you are literally related to all other living things, just as truly as you are related to your sisters and your cousins and your aunts. You share a common ancestry with every other animal and every plant; you are a product of the same long, intricate history.

The real reason for studying biology is the old admonition: "Know thyself." The better you know yourself, the happier, healthier, more comprehending, and richer will be your life. You cannot, however, really know yourself if that is all *you know. True understanding can come only from knowledge of life in general. The meaning of biology is its human meaning, its significance to you as a person, but that meaning can only be made clear if human biology is seen as a part of the biology of all life.*

Contents

Foreword by Roger Tory Peterson   ix

Preface   xv

Part 1: Time and Birds

1	The History of Life	3
2	The History of Birds	12
3	The Process of Evolution	23

Part 2: Behavior

4	Instinct	45
5	Display	57
6	Learning	64
7	The Reproductive Cycle	74
8	Social Behavior	86
9	Migration	94

Part 3: Anatomy and Physiology

10	Skin and Feathers	111
11	Bones and Muscles	123
12	Digestion	155
13	Circulation	162
14	Breathing	167
15	The Urogenital System	179
16	The Bird Brain	184
17	Hormones	190
18	The Ear	195
19	The Eye	202
20	Flight	217

Epilogue: Bird and Man   236

Suggestions for Further Reading   245

Index   251

1

Time and Birds

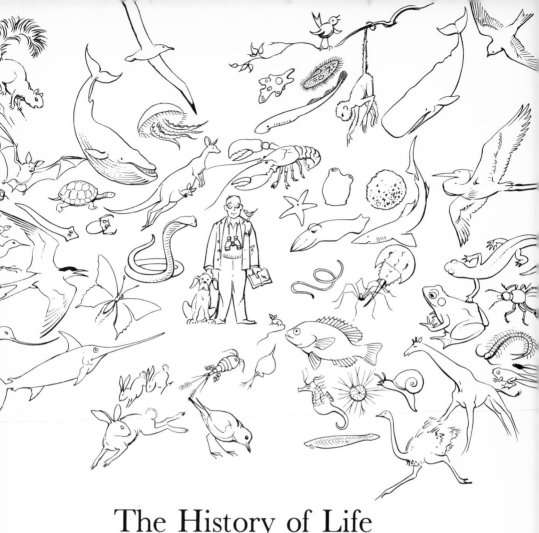

The History of Life

It is utterly impossible to comprehend the length of the time that has passed since life first appeared on earth. But some inkling of the unimaginable immensity of the age of the planet earth and the time of life upon it is necessary to understand the process that has led to the multitude of birds and other living things we see today. The entire history of man has occupied about a million years. This alone is a staggering

Geologic Time

MILLIONS OF YEARS SINCE BEGINNING	ERAS	PERIODS	EPOCHS	A FEW FEATURES OF THE LIFE RECORD		
.025	CENOZOIC	QUATERNARY	RECENT	} MAN		
1			PLEISTOCENE			
10		TERTIARY	PLIOCENE	MAMMALS & BIRDS NUMEROUS	FLOWERING PLANTS	
30			MIOCENE			
40			OLIGOCENE			
60			EOCENE			
75			PALEOCENE			
135	MESOZOIC	CRETACEOUS				
165		JURASSIC		MAMMALS & BIRDS ARISE	REPTILES NUMEROUS	
205		TRIASSIC				
230	PALEOZOIC	PERMIAN		AMPHIBIANS NUMEROUS		
255		PENNSYLVANIAN			} COAL FORESTS	
280		MISSISSIPPIAN				
325		DEVONIAN		RISE OF LAND ANIMALS, PLANTS, & TRUE FISHES - AQUATIC VERTEBRATES NUMEROUS		
360		SILURIAN				
425		ORDOVICIAN		FIRST VERTEBRATES ALL BASIC AQUATIC TYPES		
500		CAMBRIAN		FIRST ABUNDANT FOSSILS		
3000 +	PRE-CAMBRIAN			FOSSILS FEW & OBSCURE		
				ORIGIN OF LIFE		

UNKNOWN AGES BEFORE FORMATION OF ROCKS NOW EXPOSED IN CRUST OF EARTH length of time when we judge it by our usual standards of years, decades, and centuries. But in the total history of all life a million years is but a moment. Between two and three billion years ago, in the darkness of the unknown past, the first life appeared. By then the earth was doubtless already more than two billion years old.

Geologists and paleontologists have divided this time of earth into divisions representing the sequence of events in its history. Each division is determined by certain geologic happenings and by certain groups of plants and animals that lived in it. The largest division is that of the era. The length of each era is variable but each extends over 100,000,000 years, except for our own — the Cenozoic, which is still in progress. Each era has been divided into lesser lengths of time called periods and the periods of the Cenozoic, which is more accurately known, into still shorter epochs. When fossil remnants of past life are found they can be related to this geologic time scale by means of the geologic formations in which they appear.

Before a brief history of life is given it is necessary to explain how all life has been classified. Then, in conjunction with the names of the geologic divisions of time, we shall have a common language to use in talking about events incomprehensible to our momentary way of thinking.

In 1735 the Swedish naturalist Linnaeus first published his great book, *Systema Naturae*, which presented the orderly system of listing animals we use today. The Linnaean system consists of classifying into successively smaller groupings animals and plants that possess successively greater similarity to each other as a group. The largest division is that of the Kingdom. There are three Kingdoms: Protista, small organisms consisting of but one cell which are not as a group considered to be

either animal or vegetable; Plantae, plants; and Animalia,
animals. The next and smaller division is the Phylum. In the
Kingdom Animalia there are twenty-two phyla (among these,
to name but a few, are: the Phylum Porifera, sponges; Phylum
Echinodermata, spiny-skinned starfishes, sea urchins, and
their relations; Mollusca, clams, oysters, mussels, snails, etc.;
Arthropoda, joint-footed insects and crustaceans). The

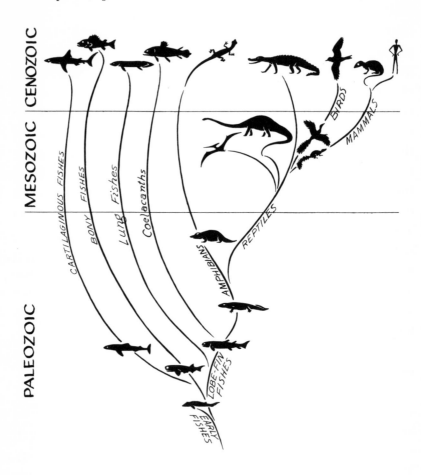

FAMILY TREE OF VERTEBRATES

phylum we are interested in is the Phylum Chordata, which includes all the animals with backbones — the vertebrates. A phylum is divided into smaller groups called Classes. The vertebrate classes are Pisces (fishes), Amphibia, Reptilia, and Mammalia, as well as the one we are concerned with, the Class Aves (birds). The next division is the Order. There are twenty-six orders of birds, and for illustration we might pick one, the Order Passeriformes, perching birds. Next comes the Family. One of the many families in the Order Passeriformes is the Family Turdidae, all thrushes. Genus is the next to last grouping. One of the genera of the Family Turdidae is the Genus *Turdus*. Finally, if we add the adjective *migratorius* to the generic name *Turdus*, we have scientifically named a species, the common American robin. Thus the robin is a bird related to other thrushes (family); who are related in a broader sense to all perching birds (order); all of whom are birds (class); and all birds have backbones and thus belong to the Phylum Chordata, which is classified under the Kingdom Animalia.

The Linnaean system is actually more complex than the above explanation. There are subphyla and sub and super divisions below and above each of the other divisions we have listed, subfamilies and superfamilies, suborders and superorders, etc. For instance, the vertebrates are a subphylum of the Phylum Chordata, the Vertebrata. But these divisions are con-

Kingdom
 Animalia
 (all animals)

Phylum
 Chordata
(with a notochord)

Class
 Aves
 (birds)

Order
 Passeriformes
(perching birds)

Family
 Turdidae
(thrushes, etc.)

Genus
 Turdus
(one of five genera)

Species
 Turdus
 migratorius
(robin)

cerned with the finer points of classification and can be ignored in order not to obscure the broad outlines of the hierarchy.

Regardless of origin, scientific names are treated as Latin nouns. They were standardized by the adoption of the *International Rules for Zoological Nomenclature* and are recognized the world over. Once learned, they are actually a lot simpler to deal with than are the multitude of colloquial names given a single species in different countries or in various parts of the same country.

When Linnaeus developed his method of listing all known life, he was recognizing the fact that living things seemed to divide naturally into groups in which all individuals were more like each other than they were like those in any other group. The only meaning that Linnaeus and his contemporaries saw in this phenomenon led them to believe that the Creator had used a different master plan for each different group and varied the members of the group within it. Then, in 1859, Charles Darwin published *On the Origin of Species*. With this great book came the gradual acceptance of the process of evolution as an explanation for the origin of the fantastic variety of living things and for their similarities as well as differences. With this revolution in thought Linnaean classification took on new meaning. It was not only an orderly and convenient system of cataloguing life but also attempted to show the nearness of relationship of groups to each other and their lines of descent from common ancestors.

The abundant fossil record of life starts in early Cambrian times, about 500,000,000 years ago, and flows without interruption from this very early period to the present. In places certain fossil links are lost; but it is not necessary to have all the pieces of a chain to know that the chain existed. Also, new links are continually being found and fitted into place. The first life must have originated two or three times as long ago as the Cambrian. Fossil algae have been found in the rocks of the Pre-Cambrian era. While algae are very primitive plants, they are a tremendous advance over what original life must have been. Many millions of years of time would have been needed to develop them. Few fossils that have proved to be animals have been found in Pre-Cambrian rocks, but very early Cambrian fossils include arthropods, which are the most complex of all the invertebrate classes and would have required millions of years to develop to this point. All the important phyla appeared before the end of the Ordovican period.

The seas were the home of the first living things. Their waters swarmed with plants and animals long before there was any life on land. Then the plants, the base of all life, gradually spread to the land. Land plants were followed by animals without backbones, the invertebrates, which also slowly evolved so that they were able to live in the air and on the vegetation that had preceded them to the land. These first land animals were ancestors to the swarms of insects and other invertebrates that plague or delight us today.

As evolution proceeded, living things developed special characteristics which enabled them to live in an ever increasing number of different ways. This increasing variety, of itself, made more variety possible. Forms developed to fill every "niche" provided by the environment — every way of making a living possible for life. In the process of photosynthesis plants use the energy of the sun to convert gases from the atmosphere and minerals of the earth into the organic stuff of their own bodies. This energy-bearing organic

matter makes possible the existence of plant-
eating animals and of nonphotosynthetic
plants; plant eaters make carnivorous animals possible; and so on, in an interdependent relationship of all life. So both the plants
and the land invertebrates created new op-
portunities for life on the land which had
never existed before. As life went on increasing in variety, certain lobe-finned fishes gave

rise to the first amphibians that crawled out
onto the land during the end of the Devonian.

During the Carboniferous period another
notable development took place — one of great
significance in the history of life. The amniote
egg developed as a major adaptation in the
evolution of the reptiles from certain early
amphibians. This tough-shelled, large-yolked
egg had many advantages. It carried the
watery conditions necessary for the life of the
embryo enclosed in its membranous amnion.
Its large yolk made a more complete development of the embryo possible. No longer did
young vertebrates have to go through a long
period of growth as comparatively helpless

water-living larvae. No longer did vertebrates have to lay their eggs in water. Vertebrates were freed from their ancient home and could fully occupy the land. And during the Jurassic period, 150,000,000 years ago, when the reptiles were nearing their peak of might and numbers, two new classes of vertebrates arose inconspicuously. Birds and small mammals evolved from two different groups of reptiles — and at just about the same time.

The History of Birds

A BIRD FLEW OUT of a palmlike tree that grew on the shore of a coral island lying in a warm tropic sea. It was about the size of a pheasant and like a pheasant flew clumsily with its short rounded wings. Its long tail did not look quite right for a bird and its head appeared to belong to some queer be-feathered lizard. By chance this strange bird flew out over the shallow water. Perhaps it was already sick and dying, or the wind was blowing too strong for its poor powers of flight. It slanted down and floundered in the few inches of water that covered a limy mud flat until, water-soaked, exhausted, and half buried, it died. In the days that followed, silt covered the bedraggled bones and feathers and they gradually disappeared.

No human could have witnessed this scene because humans had not yet evolved. But there is another incident in the history of this same bird. The coral sea has gone and the land has risen and folded into mountains. The muddy grave of the bird has hardened and compressed into the finest limestone. Men have appeared on earth and call the place Bavaria. In 1861 the limestone that had been the muddy shallow was being quarried for lithographic stone. Light fell again on the unknown bird 150,000,000 years after it had fluttered to its death.

The discovery of this exquisite fossil came at a dramatic moment. Darwin's *Origin of Species* had just been published and the controversy over evolution was at its height. Here was an animal from the past that was neither quite bird nor quite reptile. It was somewhere in between, another link in the chain of evidence that supported Darwin's historic theory. Three scientific greats of the day had a hand in describing *Archaeopteryx*, the ancient winged one, for the rest of the world. Sir Richard Owen, the great anatomist, Thomas Huxley, student, teacher, and champion of evolution, and Othniel C. Marsh, the renowned paleontologist of Yale, each studied the fossil. Eminent scientists of all nations have pored over the old bones from that day to this and tomes have been written about them. *Archaeopteryx* is known the world over.

In 1877 another fossil bird was found in the Bavarian limestone. Today both these fossils are considered by most to be the same species, *Archaeopteryx lithographica*. Some maintain that the relationship is merely that of family and call the later specimen *Archaeornis siemensi*. This distinction amounts to a scientific quibble, as does the discussion in the past about whether or not these two fossils were really birds or reptiles.

In the modern view of evolution these questions do not matter.
What is important is that there were grounds for such disagreement, proving that these fossils stood at an intermediate

stage in the gradual flow of life during which birds evolved from reptiles.

One of the most fortunate features of both fossils of *Archaeopteryx* is that impressions of feathers of both wing and tail are preserved. Without these the fossils might still be thought to be those of small reptiles. The three digits of the hand possess claws that were evidently used in climbing. The tail feathers do not radiate from a few fused tail vertebrae, as in modern birds, but from the sides of a long tail composed of about nineteen movable vertebrae. The ribs are slender and have none of the small, backward-pointing processes of bone — the uncinates — which reinforce and stiffen the rib cages of later birds. There is no keel on the breastbone, which fact, combined with the short rounded shape of the wing, indicates

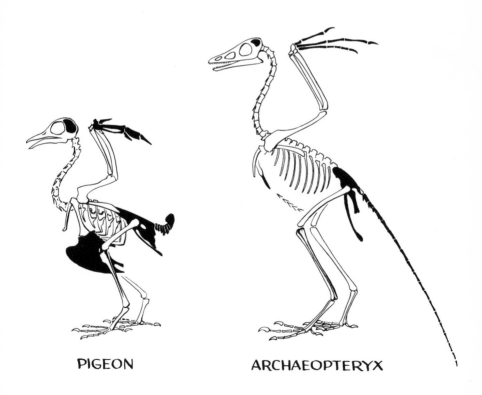

PIGEON   ARCHAEOPTERYX

that the bird had but weak powers of flight. Only a few of the vertebrae in the hip section are fused, in contrast to many in modern birds. The bones were not hollow and pneumatic and the jaws were toothed. Nevertheless, *Archaeopteryx* can be classified as a bird. It had feathers and, consequently, was undoubtedly "warm-blooded," the two principal features used to draw the line between birds and reptiles. If these fossils had never been found and an able anatomist were asked to imagine a bird in the early stages of evolution, he would come up with something very like *Archaeopteryx*.

As both the flying reptiles — pterosaurs — and small superficially birdlike dinosaurs show modifications that do not appear in birds and because these specialized types of reptiles were coexistent with *Archaeopteryx*, the ancestral reptile must have been of an earlier and less specialized type. A suitable candidate for this honor is some member of a small group of reptiles, the Pseudosuchia. The long history of birds probably started when some small species from this group became adapted for a climbing life in trees. There, the development of plane surfaces consisting of feathers, which are a modification of reptilian scales, would have

been of great advantage. Feathered forelimbs were doubtless first used for gliding and later for true flight. The clawed fingers of *Archaeopteryx* indicate that it had not progressed far enough as a flier to do away entirely with the use of its forelimbs for climbing.

In spite of the early discovery of *Archaeopteryx*, birds have not been very helpful in the study of paleontology. These light creatures of the air and trees did not often get themselves into positions where they would fossilize as had *Archaeopteryx*. The number of reasonably complete skeletons of birds that have been found is quite small in comparison to the wealth of material of most other vertebrate classes. Accurate identification of many bird fossils is very uncertain. Entire orders, families, and genera have been set up on the basis of a single bone or a few fragments. Nevertheless, Marsh dug up two very important bird fossils in 1872 from Cretaceous chalk beds of western Kansas, *Ichthyornis* and *Hesperornis*.

Enough specimens of *Hesperornis'* family, the Hesperornithidae, have been found to describe five species. These were large swimming and diving birds up to five feet or more in length, with strong, backward-pointing legs, large paddlelike feet, and long necks. The wing is known from a single humerus so small and slender that *Hesperornis* must have been flightless. The brain was comparatively small but the vertebrae were shaped like those of modern birds. *Hesperornis* lived in an area that was covered by shallow seas during the Cretaceous period. Its large legs and feet show that it must have been a strong and agile diver. The legs are so placed that they could have been of little use for walking on land. *Hesperornis* doubtless represents an already highly specialized offshoot from the line of descent leading to modern birds.

Marsh also found and first described fossils of another Cretaceous bird, *Ichthyornis*. There are seven species of this genus recognized today. These birds were about the size of a small gull, were strongly winged, and had a well-developed, deeply keeled breastbone. The neck was long and the legs comparatively weak. Brain casts of *Ichthyornis'* skull indicate that it had a definitely birdlike brain of the modern type. Although *Ichthyornis* does not take its place in the direct line of descent that has led to any modern bird, it is much closer to the main stem of bird evolution than is *Hesperornis*.

It has long been believed that both *Hesperornis* and *Ichthyornis* had teeth — those of *Hesperornis* being set in continuous grooves, while those of *Ichthyornis* were held in sockets. Both birds have consequently been placed in the superorder Odontognathae. However, further study by Joseph T. Gregory (1952) has revealed that the jaws associated with *Ichthyornis* may not have belonged to this fossil at all and probably are those of a small swimming reptile of the same

HESPERORNIS

time. So we do not know for sure whether these Cretaceous birds all had teeth or not.

The importance of these two fossils is that they show that birds had reached a high degree of specialization and diversity even at this very early time in their history. *Hesperornis*, particularly, was as specialized as is any modern bird.

As time moves forward into the Tertiary period we can use the shorter epochs. The fossil record has become more complete and age can be established more accurately. By the Eocene epoch this record has made it possible to establish tentatively fifteen orders of birds in addition to those to which *Archaeopteryx*, *Hesperornis*, and *Ichthyornis* belonged. About twelve or thirteen of these early orders have representatives alive today. Fossil evidence is still obscure in many cases, paleontologists disagree, and later evidence is also so scanty that these early specimens cannot with any great confidence always be related to later members of the orders they are thought to represent. For instance, on the strength of a single pelvis the ostrich order (Struthioniformes) is considered to have lived in the Eocene. Among other orders from the Eocene are: the now extinct elephant-birds (Aepyornithiformes), pre-pelicans (Pelecaniformes), and pre-vultures, hawks, and an eagle-like bird — *Aquilavus* (Falconiformes). Pre-herons and storks (Ciconiiformes), ancestors of the ducks, geese, and swans (Anseriformes), and chickenlike birds (Galliformes)

ICHTHYORNIS

appeared in these times. The cranes and rails (Gruiformes) were comparatively plentiful. *Diatryma*, the flightless giant nearly seven feet tall, appeared and vanished in the Eocene. Possible sandpipers and gulls represented the shorebird order Charadriiformes, and owls may have flown in the night skies of the Eocene in the form of a predecessor of the genus *Bubo*. The perching birds (Passeriformes) also appeared in these ancient days as birds that seem to be ancestral to those ranging from shrikes and others to Old World warblers.

The Oligocene epoch was a time of orderly advancing development toward recent types. True grebes, an albatross of the modern family Diomedeidae, and the genera *Puffinus*, *Anas* (surface ducks), and *Aythya* (diving ducks) were represented. There were flamingos, hawks, eagles, and vultures. There was a bird of the modern pheasant genus (*Phasianus*), and cranes, limpkins, and rails fed in the undisturbed wetlands of the time. In addition to *Bubo*, which possibly originated in the Eocene, the modern genus *Strix* was living. There were more Passeriformes than in the previous epoch, and among them were shrikes, wagtails, and a probable woodpecker.

The Miocene brought further progress toward Recent forms of bird life. The first penguin fossils have been found in deposits of this epoch; but since these birds were so very similar to the penguins of today they must have been evolving for a considerable length of time and have originated much earlier. Other birds were represented by many families and genera we know today.

The Pliocene brought additional Recent genera too numerous to mention in this brief survey, and birds of the Pleistocene ice ages are also abundantly represented by fossils. The vast majority of Pleistocene birds are of species that still survive. By the late Pleistocene almost all Recent types had evolved and become established. Also, man had come along at the beginning of the Pleistocene, so that from this time on there have been bird watchers as well as birds. It may well be that one of the qualities that made man Man was the awareness, when looking at such as a small bird, that he *had a choice* between belly-filling and his need for something more. At any rate, beautiful prehistoric cave drawings show that birds were an important part of his life one way or the other.

In looking back over the story of bird evolution as a whole, we find the change that led from reptiles to the bird we know today already well on its way in old *Archaeopteryx* of the Jurassic. In spite of the paucity of fossil evidence, we can suppose that by the Cretaceous period bird life had become abundant and diversified. *Hesperornis* and *Ichthyornis* were so highly specialized that bird evolution must have progressed a long way even before this time. The Eocene brought the great variation, or adaptive radiation, into the multitude of differing ways of life which has led directly to the birds of today. Birds were probably at their peak of variety and numbers during the Miocene and Pliocene. At that time an even, warm, humid climate prevailed over a good deal more of the earth than is the case today. The gay abundance of the Class Aves in our present tropics

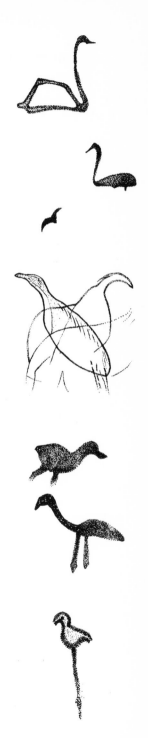

will give some idea of the variety of birds that lived over much of the world in these balmy epochs before the cold of the ice ages crept down from the poles.

The Process of Evolution

THE FOSSIL RECORD of birds, as well as that of all other
animals and plants durable enough to leave a record, points
to the fact that this slow, seemingly miraculous process of
change we call evolution has occurred. Life is no longer considered static, but dynamic; a flowing state of continual
variation that has taken place in the past is taking place
today, and will continue in the future. The study of the

process of evolution is as important in understanding the birds of today as it is to understanding the birds of the past. And, from a more personal point of view, the study of evolution has profound significance for our understanding of ourselves, our own place in nature, and our future on earth.

In looking at such a natural process it is always necessary first to take it apart in order to simplify. Nature is so complex that we cannot mentally encompass its subtle workings and interworkings. In "dissecting" evolution, as we shall later dissect the body of the bird, we must constantly keep in mind that no part of the process ever stands alone. Every feature is only a strand of a tremendous changing web of cause and effect. When we take this web apart to examine a single thread, we are likely to get a false and oversimplified view unless we always remember the whole.

Today the "how" of evolution is studied as a synthesis, the unified thinking not only of paleontology but of genetics, comparative anatomy, embryology, behavior, systematics, and so on. Here we can give only the merest outline of how evolution is believed to have taken place in birds as well as all other animals and plants.

It was not until 1859 that the science of life got its great unifying concept. As we have earlier said, in that year Charles Darwin published his great work, *The Origin of Species*. The *Origin* not only established the theory of evolution but is one of the very few books that have completely changed the direction of human thought.

Briefly, Darwin's theory of evolution was this: in natural populations many more individuals are born than can or do grow to maturity. All organisms vary slightly from one another and from their parents. In the press of competition to grow up, breed, and perpetuate the species, those with

differences that better fit them to survive this struggle are selected by nature to live and reproduce their kind. Thus, through these slight variations over the vastness of time, new species come to be through natural selection.

Darwin did not know how these variations came about or how, once they happened, they were passed on to future generations. He knew that this question left a great blank in his theory, attempted to work out and explain the mechanics of heredity, but failed. Also, his ideas concentrated on the individual rather than on groups of individuals or populations, living and breeding together. His theories were widely misunderstood and misused by others to emphasize and justify a competitive tooth-and-claw survival and the exploitation of humanity in general by a few ruthless individuals. But ruthless and aggressive humans are not necessarily the fittest in the evolutionary sense. The ability to co-operate, for instance, is one of the most important qualities in the evolution of man. Darwin himself realized that his use of the term "the struggle for existence" might be misunderstood. In the *Origin* he wrote, "I use this term in a large and metaphorical sense including dependence of one being on another . . ."

In the decade following 1859 another great biological concept was formed. Gregor Johann Mendel, an Augustinian monk, was making his immortal experiments in heredity by the breeding of peas. His report on this work, only forty pages, was published in a little-known periodical in 1866 and lay unrecognized until 1900, when Hugo de Vries of Holland, Karl Correns in Germany, and Eric von Tschermak in Vienna simultaneously rediscovered it while working on similar experiments. Mendel knew of Darwin's work (a copy of the *Origin* annotated in Mendel's hand is still in existence) but Darwin never knew of Mendel. One wonders what effect there might have been on the progress of human thought if the great naturalist had

known the results of the work of this gentle Austrian monk who, through his inspired puttering with garden peas, laid the groundwork for the science of genetics, a science that has answered the puzzle Darwin never solved.

It may seem strange to talk of a man who studied peas in a book about flying animals, creatures about as far from a vegetable as could be imagined. The very first requirement for any sort of life was the ability to copy itself, to reproduce. There could be no continuing life at all until this miracle came to be. The mechanics of heredity became established very early in the history of life and are much the same in birds as in peas. Inheritance works this way in almost all living things; within the *immature* reproductive cells of both sexes are paired units, called chromosomes, typical of all the cells of that particular species. The chromosomes contain the genes, which are the units of heredity. The genes constitute details of the inherited "plan" for the new being and control the development and chemical operation of each cell and thus the entire makeup of an organism.

When a reproductive cell becomes mature it is called a gamete. The gamete is the product of the dividing of immature reproductive cells (meiosis) in such a way that they have only one chromosome from each pair, or one half of the typical number of chromosomes for the species. The distribution of hereditary material in this process is determined purely by chance.

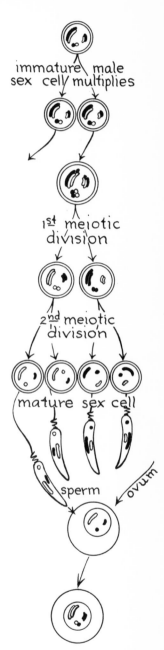

immature male sex cell multiplies

1st meiotic division

2nd meiotic division

mature sex cell

sperm   ovum

fertilized ovum

At fertilization, when a gamete from one sex unites with a gamete from the other sex, a sperm from the male and an ovum from the female, the chromosomes in each come together to total again the number of pairs typical of the cells of the species. This united set in the now fertile ovum has a random selection of the hereditary material of each parent. Thus the offspring will have a random combination of characteristics inherited from each parent, and no two offspring except identical twins are ever likely to be the same. For instance, the eight chromosomes of the tiny fruit fly used so widely in genetic experiments contain an estimated 10,000 genes or more. With only 30 gene differences there are a possible 1,000,741,824 different combinations. The number of possible combinations for 10,000 genes is astronomical. Therefore the probability that any two fruit flies — to say nothing of animals like birds — will ever have exactly the same characteristics is nil for practical purposes.

the famous fruit fly *Drosophila* and its chromosomes

actual size

In addition to the recombination of hereditary material of both parents in the offspring, brand-new hereditary material sometimes appears. Changes in the chemical composition or the arrangement of genes or chromosomes, called mutations, cause entirely new characteristics in an animal that are not inherited from its parents. These changes can, however, be passed on to future generations in the chromosomes of the animals in which they originate.

Mutations of importance occur very seldom and usually in-volve very small variations in the offspring. The vast majority are lethal or harmful to the animal possessing them. Once in a while a mutation will occur to give an animal a new quality advantageous to living. It is these new variations and their recombination from parents in offspring that are the building materials of evolution.

But what is the force that uses these materials to build the structure of evolution? In a population of interbreeding animals new characters come about through mutation. Different combinations of these with already existing charac-ters create animals with different over-all mental and physical characteristics. Because of the nature of sexual reproduction, all this occurs at random, and the frequency of occurrence in a population should be at random also. However, most populations do show regular systematic change in the fre-quency at which certain hereditary characteristics occur in succeeding generations. The fossil record shows us that birds have changed from animals like *Archaeopteryx* to those of today in a seemingly orderly way. The fact that the birds of today are not only very different but, in general, are more efficient as birds as well as tremendously more varied in their ways of life than were the Jurassic birds suggests that evolution has a preconceived direction, or a goal. Within the space of a few generations evolutionary changes are usually so slight that they cannot be told from merely random fluctuations. Over immense periods of time the total effect may be large. This effect of direction of change, which results from events that happen entirely at random, is brought about by the constant pressure of natural selection. And, in populations of a certain size and situation, this direction is toward the evolution of animals fitted to exploit new ways of life or better fitted to live similar ways of life. In other words, the direction is toward adaptation to new and different ways of living and results, of course, in new and different organisms.

This selection is called genetic selection and differs only in emphasis from the Darwinian idea. Some members of each generation have more offspring than others. Thus the hereditary material of each succeeding generation will contain more of the genes that caused the characteristics making the parent generation more successful reproducers. Successful reproduction does not mean sheer fertility. The female codfish can spawn millions of eggs, the human female can produce in a lifetime perhaps a dozen children at the most. And yet codfish are declining in numbers and the human population is exploding. The term means success in producing offspring who themselves will grow to maturity and produce offspring. This is evolutionary or genetic survival, in contrast to the survival of the individual alone. Not only individual animals but the hereditary possibilities contained in the total genetic material possessed by a population, or its gene pool, are slowly changed. The result of this slow change in the hereditary makeup is a population of organisms that is different from its ancestor population — or evolution. Evolution, we find, is not necessarily the result of individual might or fitness. It is the result of the selection of qualities that lead to efficiency in leaving progeny and the ability to cooperate with species members and thus increase the efficiency of the evolving group as a whole — not matter of sheer survival or weight of numbers alone.

The basic unit of evolution is the species. A species is a group of animals that does not, for one reason or another, interbreed to any great extent with animals of any other group. Therefore the genetic material of a species and the changes produced in it cannot be spread into the material of any other group or that of any other group into it.

No mutation or recombination of hereditary characteristics was ever great enough in one, or even a good many individuals, to create a new species — at least in complex animals. New species originate only as the hereditary material of an entire population changes. It is believed that this can happen only when a population becomes isolated from others of its original species. In time two or more such populations of a single species can vary from each other to such an extent that interbreeding will be impossible under natural circumstances. When this state is reached the two populations, which before isolation were one species, are now separate species. Continued time brings continued variation to both. Each may form additional species. The several species originating from the first of the original two will be more closely related to each other, and thus more similar, than to the group of species originating from the second of the original two. This gives rise to groups of closely related species and enables us to classify these into the artificial divisions we call genera with some degree of accuracy. Subsequent time brings further variation and splitting off and results in the establishment of the larger groups of related genera which we call families, and so on. In the meantime the original species, or larger category, from which the two evolving groups originally sprang may have become extinct. This of course obliterates the connecting links — unless they happen to turn up as fossils.

The isolation of the genetic material of one interbreeding population from that of another is necessary if speciation is to take place. Such genetic isolation is believed to always be the result of some form of geographic separation. The surface of the earth is continually changing. Populations of birds may be separated by mountain ranges, bodies of water, deserts, and other geographical factors. Segments of populations may migrate and settle areas from which they do not freely interbreed with the original population. Examples of variation occurring from isolation is very well demonstrated by birds on groups of islands separated from each other by varying distances of water.

The Galápagos Islands lie on the equator about 600 miles off the west coast of South America. They are not very old, geologically speaking — having risen from the sea about the middle of the Tertiary period — and are volcanic in origin. Their small stock of plants and animals arrived from the sea or by way of the air across at least 600 miles of open water. Except for man and his domestic animals there are only two land mammals (rats and bats), a few reptiles (including the well-known giant tortoises), and no amphibians. Birds are also poorly represented. Among them are Darwin's finches, a small subfamily of birds containing four genera with a total of fourteen species. Undoubtedly the finches originated from one ancestral species that migrated from the mainland of South America long ago. The present Galápagos genus, *Geospiza*, the ground finches, are thought to be the most similar of the present

GALÁPAGOS IS.

PACIFIC OCEAN

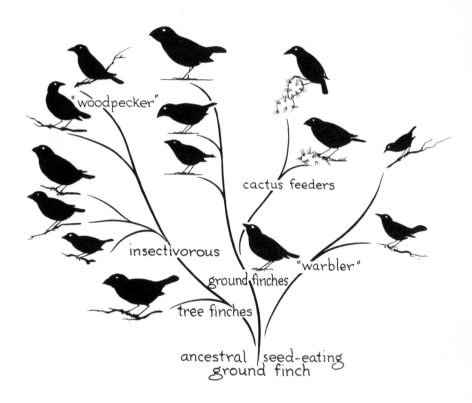

birds to the ancestral species. However, the mainland representatives of this pioneer have long been extinct.

The interesting feature of these birds is that in the absence of many competitive birds they have evolved into different species adapted to the way of life of such mainland birds as woodpeckers and warblers. From a seed-eating ancestral ground finch there have developed tree finches, insect eaters, leaf eaters, fruit and bud eaters, and cactus eaters. The chief differences between these birds is found in their beaks, which have become adapted to make possible the use of different foods and serve as recognition features.

Also, on the closely adjacent central islands there are no species or subspecies peculiar (endemic) to each island alone. In the outer islands, more and more isolated by over-water distance, the percentage of endemic species rises. It is clear that geographic isolation has caused one species to split up into many, as various populations became isolated on separate islands.

Many of the other animals of the Galápagos have undergone similar change. The Galápagos are an evolutionary laboratory, a world in miniature. There evolution can be seen in the process of happening, seen without the complications caused by the myriad species of animals abounding on the continents. This miniature example of evolution was as impressive when young Charles Darwin visited the Galápagos in 1835 as it is today. Perhaps the comparison of the finches crystallized the train of thought that was to lead to the *Origin*. At any rate Darwin gives them full credit. In the wonderful story of his early travels, told in his *Journal of Researches*, which has come to be familiarly known as *The Voyage of the Beagle*, he says of these islands: ". . . we seem to be brought somewhat nearer to that great fact — that mystery of mysteries — the first appearance of new beings on this earth"; and later of the finches themselves, "Seeing this gradation and diversity of structure in one small, intimately related group of birds, one might really fancy that from an original paucity of birds in this archipelago, one species had been taken and modified for different ends."

At this point we can make the statement that evolution is the result of the shaping of the varying genetic materials of heredity by nature's selection of those materials. The result is new sorts of animals and plants better or differently adapted to existing environments or adapted to some new environment. Adaptation is the "goal" of evolution. An adaptation is a feature or characteristic of a living thing, physical or mental, that is of advantage to it and/or to the species population of which it is a member. There has been considerable disagreement in the past as to how large a part adaptation has played in evolution. It is very difficult, many times impossible, to say whether a certain feature is adaptive or not. The adjustment of an organism to its environment is so inconceivably complex and our present knowledge of life so pitifully small that we cannot always say yes or no regarding adaptive value. Since most present-day biologists agree that almost all features of animals and plants are adaptive, we can from one point of view think of an organism as a bundle of adaptations.

The original development of the living cell with its chemical machinery was an adaptation making the processes of life possible, opening and creating of itself all the ways of "making a living" that have led to birds, men, and the countless other manifestations of life. The circulatory, respiratory, nervous, and digestive systems are adaptations that made the existence of more complex multicellular animals possible. The development of the backbone is a general adaptation resulting in vertebrate animals. The variations that resulted in the air-breathing lung and turned fins into limbs are adaptations that made it possible for vertebrate life to spread to the land. The hard-shelled large-yolked amniote egg, first developed in reptiles, was an adaptation further freeing animals from dependence on the water. The development of wings and

ADAPTIVE RADIATION

feathers was a general adaptation for flight which led to
birds. But, after these important general adaptations opened
broad new ways of life — or adaptive zones — to new kinds of
animals, further adaptive refinements evolved animals suited
to narrower adaptive zones within the limits of the original
broad one. When adaptation had led to flight as a general

way of life, further adaptive specialization resulted in more and more varieties of birds. There came to be sea birds, shore birds, soaring birds of prey, birds of the woods, birds of the fields, birds of the night, slow fliers, fast fliers, swimming birds, and even flightless birds as a secondary return to the ground or water in situations where the metabolically expensive power of flight was no longer an advantage. The adaptations which made flight possible have had a universal effect on the history, structure, physiology, behavior, and distribution of birds. All birds are what they are because they fly or have descended from ancestors that flew. Birds live in countless different ways involving countless different special adaptations of the one broad general adaptation, flight. This narrower evolution that takes place after fundamentally new types of animals have appeared is called adaptive radiation.

Extinction, as grim as it may seem, is a necessary and constructive part of evolution. If there were now alive representatives of every sort of animal that had ever existed there would not only be a dense crowd on earth, to say the least, but a blended flow of animals. Of course this is pure fancy: evolution could not have taken place without the separation between different kinds of animals that is provided by extinction. There are several modes of extinction, but they all narrow down to a single cause — changing environment. Actually, no environment is exactly the same for two consecutive moments of time. Change is the normal state of affairs and its details are endless. The "balance" of nature is a shifting balance. Change may consist of large geological events that run all the way from the instant eruption of a volcano to the gradual subsidence or rise of great or small masses of land. The area north of the Dakotas down through Texas

was once a vast sea. This now dry land abounds in fossils of fish and other sea animals. *Hesperornis* swam in these seas 135,000,000 years ago. Weather changes, climates get hotter or colder, wetter or drier. Vegetation varies and animals vary, new groups move into the territory of old and compete for space and substance. Recent warm northeastern winters have encouraged the northward spread of more southerly animals. Cardinals now winter where no cardinals wintered before, at least within man's memory or record. This warming of our climate actually may be a long-range manifestation of the waning of the last ice age, which we are still in, or it may be but a momentary fluctuation.

Competing groups may be descendant species able to outdo their relations by means of more favorable adaptations. Or they may be groups of unrelated animals that have similar adaptations developed in similar environments (parallel or convergent evolution). Replacement does not necessarily involve direct competition. Often a group of animals will have ceased to exist long before they are replaced. The mammals replaced a good many of the reptiles, but they did not do so until long after some other factor, unknown so far, had wiped out the reptiles and left empty the adaptive zones they occupied.

Species are not often driven to extinction by their predators. Most animals are so adaptively specialized that consumption of all their typical prey or food would cause their own extinction. Predation in itself is self-limiting.

Other population controls, such as epidemic disease, do not necessarily lead to extinction. There is considerable and growing evidence that many natural populations go through quite regular cycles of overcrowding and scarcity. When a population has built up to a certain density, epidemic disease may become rampant. This causes a sudden drop in numbers, abatement of the disease in epidemic form, and a gradual buildup over the years to a peak again. Evidence now seems to indicate that this "disease" is often what can only be described as shock. Cycles are well known in many species — the ruffed grouse, for example — prized by man, and thus are kept track of.

The very adaptive specialization that is the result of evolution often leads to extinction. When animals have become adapted so as to utilize only certain narrow environmental zones they often get out on an evolutionary limb if that environment fails or changes. They may have none of the genes circulating in the gene pool of their species which will make it possible to become adapted to new conditions. Highly specialized organisms that occupy narrow adaptive zones often do not have a great deal of genetic variability as a species. The very features making such organisms successful under certain conditions then become a liability under other conditions. Our common brant is a species of waterfowl that feeds largely on eelgrass. In the past this special ability to live on such plentiful food allowed the brant to exist in great numbers. However, some years ago, disease almost entirely wiped out eelgrass over most of the world. The brant almost went into extinction along with its food. Happily, the eelgrass has begun to recover and we are beginning to see flocks of brant again.

Of course many environmental changes take place so slowly that even quite specialized animals are able to change with it. Paradoxically, this process may be considered a form of extinction, because these changed animals are no longer the same beings as those that slowly vanished with the old environment.

The forces of selection need a broad base to act upon. In small isolated populations, random variations are not sufficiently controlled by selection. Harmful or nonadaptive variations often become established with increasing frequency in the genetic material of such groups. This phenomenon is called genetic drift. It may eventually lead to extinction. This may be the reason for the failure to save the last remnants of the heath hen on Martha's Vineyard. It certainly is a great danger that besets threatened populations when their numbers reach a certain low. Because of genetic drift, low-ebb species like the whooping crane and the trumpeter swan may find it impossible ever to increase to really safe numbers

again. This feature also complicates the preservation on isolated refuges of large mammals of normally low numbers.
Actually genetic drift is also due to change in environment,
the genetic environment of the population itself.

There is a widely misunderstood feature of evolution.
Ducks, for example, did not develop webbed feet *so that they
could swim;* they can swim *because they developed webbed feet.*
This is not a quibble but a very important point. Gene mutations arose in a population of birds to cause development of
webs between the toes. This new hereditary characteristic
gave the birds that had it the opportunity to exploit a new
way of life. Once started on this adaptive path, those
members of the population whose hereditary characteristics
increased the efficiency of the webbed feet had an advantage
that enabled them to prosper and pass this quality on to new
generations. And so the genes for webbed feet became more
and more frequent in the evolving population from generation to generation. Of course this is an oversimplification.
Many other adaptations have made it possible for ducks to
lead the way of life they do today. But the point is that
hereditary changes *come first.* They become adaptations only
when they are preserved in the gene pool and become more
and more frequent as generation succeeds generation. The
demands of the environment have no effect whatever as far as
causing specific mutations or recombinations is concerned.
The environment can only select from among those mutations or recombinations that have happened to arise entirely
by chance.

The complexities of the process of evolution are endless.
It would be impossible to describe them adequately without
mentioning innumerable causes and innumerable effects.
We must simply say that every tiny facet of life affects every

other facet, small or large; all these are constantly changing and influencing each other in new ways; and the whole of the present and future is limited and modified by every facet that has existed in the past. The web of life is an incalculably intricate fabric. We humans are inextricably woven into it. The buildings and people of Main Street are as much a part of it as are the wild birds of the deepest jungle.

2

Behavior

Instinct

ALL SCIENCES have not progressed to the same degree.
Physics and inorganic chemistry are far ahead of biology.
Perhaps, in spite of its obscurities, physics is really "easier"
than biology. Physics is the study of the phenomenon of lifeless matter and of energy. Biology is the study of that same
lifeless matter and energy in a more highly organized form —
organic matter and living energy. Perhaps, also, living

organisms are more subject to those stultifying human traits, tradition, superstition, and wishful thinking.

Some branches of biology also have been established longer and have progressed further than others. Gross anatomy had its flowering long ago and was a highly developed science before 1900. Genetics can be said to have been born with the work of Mendel and to have existed as a science only since 1900. The most difficult study of all is that of the hidden, intricate, fantastically subtle workings of the mind. Psychology (often defined as the science of behavior) is not ordinarily considered to be one of the biological sciences. However, behavior is what an organism does, how it reacts to stimuli from the environment, from other living things, and from within itself. It is impossible to study behavior significantly without a good knowledge of all the other manifestations of life; it is impossible to study the other manifestations of life without a good knowledge of behavior. Behavior also is an infant science, still groping with all the uncertainty of ignor-ance. There still are endless blank spots in all branches of biology. In the behavioral sciences, supposition and hypothe-sis are almost the rule. The pages ahead will be thickly sprinkled with supposes, perhaps, possibilities, and maybes, as well as much personal opinion and speculation.

In ordinary usage the word instinct has several indefinite meanings. Often we say, "I jammed on the brakes instinc-tively," but this quick unthinking action is not an instinct in the biological sense of the word. It is a habit, carefully learned and repeated so many times that conscious thought is no longer needed to perform it. An example of the correct use of the word is to say "A mammal baby sucks its mother's nipple instinctively" or "a baby bird gapes with open mouth instinc-tively." Baby mammals and baby birds are born with these abilities and use no learning, reason, or experience to acquire them. Instinct is the inherited tendency to act in a certain way in response to a certain situation. It is as stereotyped and inflexible as is the inherited tendency for an animal to be a certain size, shape, or color.

In man and, to a lesser degree, in other mammals learning tends to modify or disguise these unlearned and inherited traits we call instincts, the fundamental base of all behavior. But birds' actions are regulated by means of instinctive or innate behavior to a much greater degree than are those of most mammals. Learning processes are employed to a *comparatively* small extent. Consequently birds are ideal subjects through which to study instinct.

Instinct is a name for something we cannot as yet explain. It is easy enough to say that a bird migrates because of instinct. This merely gives a name to our ignorance. So, until we know more about life than at present, we must simply assume that the innate qualities peculiar to the nervous and endocrine systems of an animal are qualities inherited in the same way as the physical characteristics. With some knowledge of the anatomy, physiology, evolution, and ecology of an animal we can deduce a good deal of the mechanical how and why of this unknown quantity through careful, objective observation of the animal's activities in both the wild and the laboratory. .

Emotion is, of course, a subjective matter. We can only *know* that it exists or how it "feels" in ourselves. So we cannot study it objectively in nonhuman animals. In saying that most bird activity is governed by instinct, we do not mean to be unsentimental and cold-blooded concerning the emotions of birds. It is almost a fad nowadays to consider anthropomorphism (the endowment of subhuman animals with human emotions and standards) a scientific sin. This tendency has

reached such proportions that there is a mis-
conception of the term misleading to the whole
science of psychology, human or otherwise. It
has tended to make us think of these animals as
machines and to separate completely their mental processes from our own. But no one can say
that basically the strong love of a human mother
for her child is not much the same "emotion"
as the love of a mother bird for her nestling.
For instance, there is a strong attraction in
humans for babies of all species. The infant
shape of puppies, chicks, kittens, bunnies, or
almost any baby in addition to the human ones
releases an emotion in man of protection and
love. Many Disney cartoons exploit the universality of this appeal. The "feeling" is necessary to the very survival of the species, since it
results in the invariable protection of the young,
the future of the species. It is an instinct in
man just as surely as it is an instinct in birds.
It is released by the same sign in both birds and
man, the helpless, cuddly baby shape. This is
doubtless why the baby shape of a duckling
appeals to us as much as to a mother duck.

Human beings are inclined to feel indignant
when they are told that they do something
morally estimable because of an instinct and
not because of virtue. We much more readily
admit that our sins are instinctive. In addition
to the love of young there are other instincts
that are also emotional — like fear and aggression. They too are adaptations favorable to

existence. An animal without fear or aggression could not live at all. Human virtue or ethics come into the picture when we select with our conscious minds or through the influence of upbringing the socially approved outlets for our instincts. The drive that causes a doctor to fight disease contains aggression just as do the acts of an antisocial person; but the doctor is "good" because he is fortunately able to direct his aggression in a constructive direction. The difference between us and the "lower" animals is that we cover our instincts with reason and/or rationalization. We make conscious virtues (and sins) out of them. We write poems, songs, and stories about them. We are able to deny, with greater or less strain, many instincts when the gratification of the drives they create are harmful to ourselves, our society, or contradictory to our traditions. Birds cannot reflect upon or deny their instincts or call them emotions. They have not evolved mentally to be able to do so. In order to understand behavior and its evolution it is better to turn anthropomorphism around and say: humans have inherited many of the instincts of subhuman animals, just as they have inherited homologous anatomical and physiological features; these instincts can be more easily studied in those simpler beings whose basic behavior is not modified by that extra, wonderful mental quality that makes man something considerably more than "just an animal."

The nuptial flight
of eagles

The fact that most bird activities are innate has been shown countless times by raising individuals without contact with others of their species from the egg onwards. Such birds invariably perform almost every typical activity of their species in the same way and at the same time as their parent-raised siblings (brothers and, collectively, sisters). They fly, feed, mate, nest, rear young, and do other very complex things in a manner identical with that of others of their species. Domestic fowl are almost entirely hatched in incubators today and never have any opportunity to learn anything from parents or elders. Yet they invariably grow up to lead typical and efficient chicken lives. Many wild species almost never associate with old birds of their kind after leaving the nest. Yet they are able to migrate, mate, nest, and raise their own offspring with success.

It is difficult to realize how complex behavior patterns such as the involved courtship dances and flights of some birds or the structurally complicated nests built by many of the passerines could ever have come about as unlearned abilities. But the behavior evolved as favorable adaptations just as did the physical adaptive characteristics. It is even more difficult to realize that these instinctive actions are done with no need for knowledge of what the outcome of the actions will be in the mind of the bird. All observable evidence points to the fact that the bird does not use insight or foresight in connec-

tion with most of its activities. When a nest is built there is
no knowledge of the purpose or of what the results of nest
building will be. For example, it would be impossible for all
nests of a species for hundreds of thousands of years over vast
geographical areas, to be built in almost exactly the same way
with the same materials by every bird of that species if the
bird first thought, "My mate is going to lay eggs. Therefore
a receptacle is needed to hold them until they hatch. Now let
me see — twigs, grass, a dab of mud and old feathers ought to
do the trick." Inevitably there would be as many different
kinds of nests among one species as there are of dwellings
among men. The very nature of innate behavior works in
such a way that no foreknowledge of a goal or the use of reason in attaining it is needed. The nervous system simply follows, as it reacts to the environment, the inherited behavior
of the species, just as the body follows during growth the inherited physical pattern. How wonderful to have evolved a
nervous system that solves all problems without any worry or
brain fatigue; especially handy for small, short-lived animals
whose brain capacity is largely devoted to such physical functions as sight and coordination. Think of the strain removed
if man could but live this way, although then we would be
"nothing but" animals indeed, with none of the joyous and
painful power of reason and resulting responsibility for our
actions.

Inherited behavior works well only just so long as the bird
is confronted with problems and situations that are within the
norms of the way of life its species has become adapted to in
the course of millions of years of evolution. Bird behavior is
so efficient that it seems impossible at first thought to inter-
pret it as anything else than the result of reasoned actions
aimed at a particular goal. Individual birds, nevertheless, are

quite inflexible in their behavior when they meet situations not fitting the scope of these inherited abilities. When confronted with unusual problems the bird will often go right ahead with its regular inherited activity in spite of the fact that it is often ridiculously inappropriate to the situation. Penguins, adapted to recognize instinctively the shrimp they feed upon when it is moving in the water, will sit quietly on land and starve to death beside a heap of the same fresh shrimp. Captive penguins must be carefully conditioned to accept food on land by being force fed for a long time.

Many aspects of instinctive behavior seem so peculiar to us that writers often refer to birds as living in a strange and separate mental world. Whether or not it is really strange or only the result of our peculiar way of thinking about ourselves is beside the point here. It does *seem* strange. David Lack's experiments with mounted birds during his study of the European robin will serve as an example. The robin is a territorial bird. That is, during the breeding season a male establishes a certain area which he guards against trespass by all other members of his species except his mate. The reason for territorial behavior of this sort is not entirely clear. It has probably evolved in order to assure a thin distribution of breeding pairs as a guard against overcrowding with inadequate food supply. To some extent territoriality is a limiting factor for total population numbers. Those members of a species excluded from a satisfactory territory do not usually breed successfully and are extra-vulnerable to predation. Also, the even distribution of birds resulting from territorial behavior may well make the location of mates easier and in some cases provide mutual stimulation. The fighting employed to repel invaders does not ordinarily go beyond a certain ritualized posturing or display that seems to communicate threat satis-

Hypothetical territorial boundaries of three pairs of house wrens

factorily. The invader usually flees the moment he is confronted by the territory owner in the threat display of his
species — an admirably economical way to conduct war.
When Dr. Lack wired a stuffed robin close to the nest of a
pair of breeding birds they postured at it in the usual robin
way. When it did not leave they attacked violently. Obviously the stuffed robin did not behave or really even look like

a live rival. But the typical instinctive behavior with which robins establish and defend their territories was triggered by the shape and color of a third "robin" in the area.

The most revealing part of these experiments happened when an especially aggressive robin attacked the stuffed specimen, beheaded it, and continued to attack as violently as ever. The hint given by this incident led to a series of trials using only parts of mounted robins or entire specimens painted in colors other than normal. These trials led to the discovery that breeding robins tended to attack or threaten only mounts or parts of mounts that included red breast feathers. Many reacted to a bundle of red breast feathers alone much more readily than to complete mounted robins whose breasts had been stained some other color.

How is it that a bird seemingly intelligent and perceptive enough to know that a stranger should be driven away for the good of the family could act in such a stupid fashion? The

answer is not that robins don't have efficient sight or other perceptions. A male easily learns to tell his practically identical mate from all other robins. Robins can even recognize human individuals they are acquainted with. The only answer can be that the part of the bird's nervous system that is intelligent is not utilized during this behavior and its maximum perceptive abilities are not flexible enough to be brought into play in so unusual a situation. Robins have become adapted to react innately at the sight of red feathers in their territories, which trigger or release aggressive behavior toward the bird to whom the red feathers belong. Only that part of the nervous system containing this pattern of behavior is affected. It is solely affected by the sight of red feathers that do not behave like those of the robin's mate. Thus it does not matter much, as far as releasing the appropriate innate behavior is concerned, whether the rest of the rival robin is present or not. This fact does not register on the attacker's consciousness because he is not employing a conscious reaction. He is adapted to attack red feathers innately.

Under normal circumstances such innate behavior works with wondrous efficiency. It does not require the excess baggage of learning or thinking to enable the bird to accomplish its purpose. Almost never, under natural circumstances, would a robin encounter conditions causing behavior to go awry as it did in these experiments. The birds only have become adapted to "normal" conditions.

Thousands of other tests similar to these have been made with birds and other classes of animals which show in the same way that a good deal of animal behavior is of this innate type. It works so well under normal circumstances that it seems wonderfully intelligent. We call it "the wisdom of the wild" and such phrases. It is not until we interfere, as did

Dr. Lack, by creating some abnormal situation that we find the behavior of the bird not intelligent and purposeful but inflexible and inadequate for other than a situation to which the species has become adapted by long evolution.

Display

THE WORD DISPLAY, as used in the study of behavior, means the showing off of certain physical features, the performance of certain actions, or the making of sounds innate and common to the species. Display communicates to mate, species member, or — rarely — other species members, the instinctive intentions or state of the bird and causes proper instinctive responses. Display is responsible for much that we consider beautiful in birds, from their marvelous song, through a kaleidoscope of color, to such fantastically beautiful motions as the flashing spread of the male peacock's tail coverts. In the study of animal behavior it is a rule of thumb that if a species has an outstanding brightly colored mark or characteristic, this feature is bound to be used in display.

These bright markings or colors are prevalent in male birds of many species, whereas females are often inconspicuous. It used to be supposed that the showier, more expendable males attracted predators away from nest, female, and young. However, the growing knowledge of bird behavior shows that the principal function of conspicuous coloration is in visual courtship display. Bright patterns and hues tend to be common among males of closely related species inhabiting the same, or overlapping, breeding areas. A good example of this tendency can be seen in the plumage of the surface-feeding ducks. The appearance of the males of the various species is quite distinct, while that of the females is subdued and much more similar. On the other hand the appearance of ducks of closely related species not inhabiting the same breeding areas, such

mallard　　　　　　pintail　　　　　　American
　　　　　　　　　　　　　　　　　　　widgeon

black duck   mottled duck

as the black and mottled duck, is not nearly as distinctive, either between species or the sexes of the same species. Such definite plumage differences doubtless aid in quick and accurate species recognition between potential mates, preventing undue hybridization and increasing the efficiency of mating performances generally. Also, there are many indications that among males of a species those with the brightest colors and patterns are more efficient in gaining mates and in carrying out the intricate patterns of the breeding cycle. These advantages resulting from conspicuous coloration obviously offset the disadvantages coming from the loss of protective coloration.

Knowledge of display in many different species is much too great even to outline here. The communal dances and mass display of social birds like penguins, sandhill cranes, or gannets seem to stimulate the entire group. The males of many gallinaceous species meet at dancing grounds and strut before the females, which apparently pick the most desirable individuals to mate with. The males of the ruff also meet at traditional "leks" and display for females. There is evidence that those males with the most conspicuous features are chosen most often by the females. The ducks utilize their striking plumage in long elaborate courtship performances. The yellow-shafted flicker has a fine, postured dance, which —

the bird with skyward pointed head, swaying body, and breast swelled to exhibit best the beautiful sickle mark of black — is in its way as stately and thrilling as the more exotic spread-winged performance of the wandering albatross or the incredibly intricate building project of the bowerbird. The strutting and cooing and billing of the common pigeon is bird display that can be witnessed in any city park. And familiar to many is the courtship of the barnyard cock, which shuffles about the hen, wing spread and dragging, to show the greatest possible expanse of bright color and pattern.

There is a very curious element in display. Sir Julian Huxley was probably the first to recognize it when, in his study of the courtship habits of the great crested grebe in 1914, he mentioned "habit preening." Later he proposed the term "ritualization" for this and similar peculiarly stereotyped behavior traits. In the midst of many such ceremonies, birds will often break off suddenly and perform some completely unrelated activity. Fighting cocks stop and peck for food, threatening gulls pull weeds, other birds preen or sleep. This sort of behavior has been called displacement activity. It seems to take place when a bird is hesitating between two equally strong drives or is frustrated in carrying out some action. In other

words, it seems that the energy for the pattern of a certain innate action becomes surplus when it cannot be normally released or used, and sparks over into the pattern of some other behavior not always appropriate to the reality of the moment.

In territorial disputes it is a general rule that a bird well within its own territory always wins a fight with an intruder. Ordinarily he has only to sing or present the threat display of his species to rout the invader. If the same two birds come together under reverse circumstances, the second puts the first to flight as easily as he himself was previously vanquished. There seems to be a moral advantage among birds and baseball players in being on home grounds. However, when these same birds come together near the boundaries of their adjacent territories this advantage tends to cancel out. It is in such a situation that a great deal of displacement activity takes place. At a location where exact boundaries may be doubtful, the drive to defend the territory and the drive to flee from another's become perfectly balanced. The bird then cannot decide which action to take and must release pent-up energy in some other activity.

When a bird is frustrated in performing some drive, displacement activity also frequently takes

place. It is not unusual to see male birds suddenly commence preening, eating, or sleeping when the female does not respond properly to the stimuli of the male's actions. In these cases too the energy of the drive cannot be used and seems to have to be released through the safety valve of displacement activity.

Many other classes of animals resort to displacement. In man, head scratching, ear pulling, coin jangling, key twirling, nail biting, and like signs of nervousness can be considered as displacement motions.

In birds, whose life is so dominated by innate behavior, many different signals have had to evolve with which to communicate and trigger instinctive actions. Actually, these signals constitute a good part of the so-called language of the birds. They must be distinct and easily and clearly recognizable so that individuals will respond correctly to the behavior of their fellows and mates. Many signals stem from regular motions connected with the activity or intention movements, taking place. For instance, numerous threat signs are formalized instinctive motions of actual intention to attack, or of aggression; but many displacement activities seem to have become unrelated to the original psychological situations that created them. They also have become formalized, stereotyped gestures that indicate only the bare form of the activity they were derived from. They appear frequently in courtship ceremony and have taken their place as a regular part of the display typical of and instinctive to a species. In the course of evolution the need for so many distinct signals has caused the "borrowing" of displacement activities and their incorporation into the regular set of other signals, used as innate releaser mechanisms. The fact that so many of the particular activities used in this manner bring prominent features of the bird anatomy into play, so as to make the movement very conspicuous, substantiates this. During courtship the male mallard goes through motions unmistakably derived from displacement preening. As he thrusts his head over his back, the wing is slightly spread and the beautiful white-edged iridescent blue speculum is flashed before the female. The mandarin duck makes a single stroke with its bill along the specialized broad tan secondary feather. This motion would be unrecognizable as having been derived from displacement preening if the motion were not known in the mallard. Other similar examples can be found in the courtship and aggressive behavior of many other species. Niko Tinbergen has termed this second category of displacement activity "derived activity." Many actions of display that seem to have little or no relation to any functional reality may well be derived activities that have become incorporated in the behavior pattern of the species by natural selection. These activities often have been ritualized to such an extent that any resemblance to the actions from which they originated has disappeared.

Learning

NONE BUT the most simple animals can possibly exist by means of completely inflexible instinctive behavior. In each creature there must be some individual adaptability, or learning ability, no matter how small. No two situations in life are ever identical enough for absolutely rigid instincts to be adequate in dealing with them. Compared to the whole gamut of animal life, birds' ability to learn is quite high. In the laboratory they have been trained to perform quite complex actions in order to obtain rewards of food. Chickens quickly learn to eat only every other grain of corn from rows in which every second kernel has been glued fast. But when the alternate kernels are no longer glued the birds continue to eat every other grain for some time. There are many other examples of similar but even more complex learning in birds.

In the wild, recognition of territory, nest location, of mates and offspring as individuals, of places or situations that signify danger, and the location of local food supplies are some of the many things learned. Also, instincts are modified by learning as birds learn to fly better with experience, build better nests in their second season, or conduct the intricate steps of the breeding pattern more efficiently. Some birds imitate the sounds of others, as do parrots and mockingbirds. Many species must learn their typical song. Young male nightingales will not learn to sing nightingale song when raised apart from males of their species. When isolated from their kind they will adopt the song of almost any species they happen to hear. Young nightingales are adapted instinctively to learn the song sung by the birds they most closely associate with but do not know their species song instinctively. Under natural conditions young nightingales always associate with other nightingales. When these young birds have learned the wrong song first, by being artificially confined with singing males of different species, they will, when exposed to the regular singing of nightingales later, quickly learn their proper species song. Other birds, like the swallow and grasshopper sparrow, inherit their specific song and can be made to sing no other. David Lack noticed that the male European robin increased his singing a great deal just after the nestlings flew but while they were still under parental care. He suggests it is at this time that the young birds learn robin music, although they do not actually sing themselves until much later.

It is difficult always to tell whether certain behavior is learned, is innate, or a combination of both. One method of distinguishing, by raising birds in isolation and comparing their behavior to that of wild species, has already been mentioned. In the wild state individual differences are a good indication of learned behavior. However, it cannot be taken for granted that a reaction is innate because it is the same throughout a population. Learning can occur under such similar circumstances that the behavior of all members of a species becomes almost identical. Birds learn very quickly to avoid inedible insects, but unless observations have been made of the young trying and rejecting these one might easily assume that the avoidance was innate. It is also easy to confuse learning with innate behavior appearing only at certain stages of growth. In an experiment on the reactions of ducklings and goslings to models of birds of prey it was found that the ducklings reacted to the models when very young but that the goslings had to depend upon the alarm calls of the adults to tell them of danger. These later on began to react to the models without warnings from the old birds. It could be reasonably concluded at this point that the goslings had learned to recognize this danger by associating it with the alarm calls of the adults. Since good scientists never take anything for granted, the experiment was carried further. Goslings were raised without ever having heard or seen a mature goose. These birds began to react to the prey models at exactly the same period of their development as did the goslings raised with their parents. So the reaction was determined to be innate after all, and merely appears later in geese than it does in ducks.

Generally birds are very poor at learning by imitation, with the exception of those that learn their songs or imitate songs of other species. Caged birds will almost never notice an opening in an enclosure when one of their number accidentally finds and uses it for escape. Last winter, after a heavy snowfall, a covey of seven quails came in to feed on cracked corn that we scatter about near our kitchen garden. The

garden is surrounded by a low barrier of chicken wire to ex-
clude members of our thriving woodchuck colony in the summer. During their feeding the quails somehow got into the
garden. When we first saw them, all seven were frantically
running along the wire trying to find an opening in it. Finally
one bird hopped up over the wire and made off. All the others
continued their desperate search in spite of the fact that they
had plainly seen the first bird escape. One by one each had
to discover the way out for itself, until one last small bird
went over the wire and disappeared minutes behind the rest.

Without stretching the true complexity of the situation too much we can say, simply, that there are three ways in which animals learn — conditioning, trial and error, and (rarely) insight or reasoned learning. Conditioning is learning to accept a *different* or *new* sign as a stimulus for certain behavior. The resulting behavior usually remains the same. Our tame cedar waxwing, Rima, quickly learned that food was coming when one of us picked up her empty dish and left the room. She invariably met us at the door when we returned with the full dish. Ordinarily only the sight of food itself would mean anything to this bird, but she had learned to accept our departure and return, dish in hand, as a signal that food was available.

Trial-and-error learning is an exploratory method. The animal tries a number of alternatives in solving a problem and hits upon the solution by accident. When this process has been repeated a number of times the animal learns to select the correct solution the first time. Rima would invariably try all berries offered her by crushing them in her bill and tasting. Those that were not suitable were rejected. If the same berries were offered later she would again taste them all. It was not until after several tries that the bird would learn to reject or accept a berry by sight and swallow it without tasting.

Insight, like trial-and-error learning, selects the proper response for the solution of a problem. Insight takes place suddenly and appears to eliminate the process of trying and rejecting alternatives. Decisions are often made at once, as experience of similar but different problems is associated and reorganized in the mind. It is problematical whether or not birds are capable of any insight.

We shall discuss imprinting here because it is usually considered a form of learning. If imprinting is learning, it is a very special kind. Konrad Lorenz found that newborn graylag geese recognize and accept the first large moving object they see as their proper parent. In the normal course of events, this large object is the mother goose. When Lorenz raised graylags in an incubator and presented himself to them as they hatched they "learned" instantly to identify him as their proper parent. They followed him everywhere, including the Danube for frequent companionable swims, in preference to following their own mother and other geese.

Imprinting of a similar kind takes place in many different species as widely separated as are insects, fish, and mammals. "House" sheep — those cared for at the farmhouse when orphaned at birth or shortly afterward — ever afterward prefer the society of humans to that of other sheep.

Recent work by E. H. Hess and his associates with mallard ducklings and chickens has demonstrated many additional details. Hess found that the critical age at which imprinting was most effective was between thirteen and sixteen hours with the mallards. Effectiveness increased up to this time in proportion to the bird's ability to get about. Animals are born without apparent fear of other living things and show none during the first few hours of their lives. Hess has also shown that the effectiveness of imprinting ends with the onset of fear, which appears at different ages in different animals and prevents the "social" contacts and "trust" necessary for imprinting. Also, the strength of imprinting does not depend on the *duration* of the imprinting period so much as it does on the *effort* expended or the distance walked by the duckling in following the imprinting object — in this case a male mallard decoy. Ducklings that had to struggle over obstacles as they followed made higher scores in subsequent tests than those following over an unobstructed path for the same distance. Hess has called this phenomenon the "law of effort."

Imprintability is doubtless a hereditary factor. Preliminary experiments have indicated that the first-generation offspring of ducks that imprinted well show scores significantly better than do the offspring of nonimprinters. Highly domesticated animals often lose many of the adaptive behavior traits of their wild ancestors because they are no longer subject to selection for these by nature or by man. Leghorn chickens, for instance, will hardly brood eggs at all; the continuation of their race depends upon the incubator. Also, Leghorn imprintability is notably poor.

Imprinting occurs at a certain fixed age in a young animal and requires a comparatively short time to take effect when compared to ordinary learning. It is considered by many investigators to be irreversible. Like instinctive traits, its details are similar in all members of a species. Imprinting can thus be defined as an innate disposition to learn quickly a certain thing at a certain time in a certain way peculiar to a certain species. Its effectiveness depends upon effort expended during one experience — not upon repeated short experiences, as does regular learning. Thus imprinting cannot be considered as true learning, which is a comparatively long individual process. It is probably a supplement to the system of inherited innate recognition of signs that stimulate and release mechanisms controlling so much of behavior.

Our own experiences with imprinting have been less scientific, perhaps, but more intimate. This year, for instance, the old hen mallard got off in her timing. She quit the nest when only two ducklings were ready and left eight unhatched eggs to cool. When we investigated, all of the eggs were pipped or showed other signs of life. After some warming in the oven and a little assistance in hatching we had seven healthy ducklings fluffed out, rested, and ready to join their two siblings. The eighth egg when "peeled" produced a duckling so small and weak that it obviously wasn't capable of competing with all its brothers and sisters. So, with two normal ducklings for company, it went into a cardboard carton with a heating pad for warmth.

Here was a fine opportunity to imprint some mallards for our own wonderment. But the critical fourteenth hour for imprinting fell late that evening and we had tickets for a long antic-

ipated performance of summer-theatre Shakespeare. Our
young ducks finally got imprinted at midnight and did not
seem to be in the least disturbed by the hour, our best clothes,
or a festive air with faint Elizabethan echoes. Each of them
unhesitatingly and faithfully followed a crouching, slowly
moving, loudly quacking, somewhat sheepish human over
pillows and books about the living room for fifteen minutes
and then was put to bed.

From that time on, with the assistance of the faithful heating pad, either one of us *was* the ducklings' parent. They had
immediately identified a quacking human as their mother.
They were so attached to us that all three shrieked in chorus
with their shrill, penetrating *weep weep weep* distress call of
abandoned ducklings if one or the other of us was not nearby
in their every waking instant. They followed us about everywhere as we gardened or went for short walks. Any sufficiently indulgent human would do for a "mother." On several
occasions kind friends "duck sat" for us when we had to be
away together. When relieved, the friends always seemed a
bit dazed by what appeared to be the inconceivable flattery
of having three small mallards follow their every move, sleep
on their feet, fondly bite their shoelace tips, or frantically *weep*
when they got more than five feet away. The ducklings gave
a psychiatrist friend their full performance one day. "Good
heavens, it's magic! They think I'm their mother," he said,
and offered to treat them gratis if the experience had unduly
confused their personalities.

When they were almost a month old we introduced them
to their proper parents and left them. The old female responded to their *weep* call at once. But the ducklings fled
from this monster in haste, and, when one of us quacked from
a distance, rushed gratefully to us. Nevertheless, they were

as at ease with their unimprinted, to humans, siblings as they were with each other. Gradually, as the ducklings matured, they became more and more independent, just as they would have in outgrowing the need for their duck mother. When well along in adolescence and turned into the duckyard for good, they no longer showed fear but threatened and at first dominated the old ducks. Slowly they learned to accept the strange large birds.

At the moment our ducklings are almost fully grown and quite independent, although they are much more friendly to humans than are unimprinted mallards. As imprinting must play a very large part in the mental adjustment by which animals later identify their fellows and their mates, we wonder what the effect of this experience will be when our three mallards come to choose their partners and breed next spring.

The Reproductive Cycle

THE MOST INTERESTING and revealing aspects of bird behavior take place during the reproductive cycle. An account
of a generalized pair of birds will demonstrate the way in
which innate behavior tends to take place in patterns or se-
quences. As the breeding season approaches, the male, stimulated by the effect of the lengthening days of spring, migrates.
He arrives at the breeding grounds early and establishes a
territory. This he guards from all others of his species by singing, which serves the dual purpose of warning off other males
and attracting females, and by fighting, as already described
in David Lack's experiments with the European robin.

The female arrives somewhat later and is attracted by his
song. At first he may threaten her in much the same way as
he does other males, but the female will not respond as does

another male. She neither fights nor flees; she displays to the male in a manner unique to females of her species. The female reaction seems to allay the aggressive male drive, identify sex, and bring on acceptance. As a rule acceptance occurs gradually. It takes time to switch male aggression to acceptance and to overcome a certain amount of fear common to both sexes. Also, time is needed for the pair to learn to recognize each other as individuals. Often some mutual display continues even after the young are born. Apparently display not only initiates the bond but maintains it and provides mutual stimulation in reaching full breeding condition.

An interesting part of many courtship ceremonies is courtship feeding. The female begs food in very much the manner of a young nestling. The male either regurgitates food or gives it from his bill, depending upon how the species feeds the young. Courtship feeding also seems to strengthen the pairing bond and stimulate sexual drives. It has no obvious connection with the impending feeding of young, since it takes place long before this duty is necessary. There may be some emotional tie or "memory" between it and the "love" through

feeding received when the bird was young. Or, perhaps, in ages past it had adaptive value in supplying food to the female who was about to take on the extra metabolic duty of producing eggs. In its present form, hardly enough food is involved to matter. Nevertheless, the ceremony is quite common among widely separate species of birds. Even domestic cocks will "find" food for the hen and cluck over it invitingly until she comes. In pigeons courtship feeding has become so ritualized that food does not enter into the act at all. The ceremony consists only of billing. Birds ordinarily seem to fear to an extreme degree being touched even by members of their own species. As close physical contact is necessary in mating, the contact of ceremonial feeding may have great value in diminishing this fear. Whatever the reason, it is obviously of value to the many species who use it during courtship. In many it takes place not only a long time before coition but during nest building, egg laying, and incubation. This does seem to suggest that at some time during bird evolution courtship feeding was of a utilitarian nature in supplying food to the female too busy to hunt for herself and needing extra food for the creation of her large-yolked eggs. Courtship feeding probably is, like many of these ceremonies, a ritualized remnant of a once practical activity that now serves as a sign or signal to stimulate a new behavior phase (acceptance of close contact between individuals) or to extinguish an old (the natural fear of being touched).

The next step in the reproductive cycle is actual coition. It may be preceded by elaborate displays in some species or almost imperceptible posturing in others. Often this consists merely of squatting on the part of the female. Ruffed grouse will attempt to copulate with stuffed specimens, dead grouse, or even other males so long as the *pose* of the bird is flattened

or crouching. This might lead one to think that grouse can't tell the difference between male and female. But grouse can and do distinguish between sexes, and even individual birds in other phases of behavior. Unlike the robin attacking at the sight of red feathers whose *color* stimulated appropriate behavior, the male grouse is stimulated to act by certain *behavior*. Thus a certain action can also serve as a sign to stimulate innate activity.

Nest building may be done by the male and female cooperating or by the female alone. In some species the male builds one or several nests before the female arrives. Nests vary from simple hollows, or scrapes, in the ground to the complex structures of orioles and weaverbirds. The more elaborate nest-building performances were once considered prime examples of intelligent and purposeful activity. But nest building also is innate. The bird does not learn it. Weaverbirds raised in isolation for several generations continued to build regular weaverbird nests.

When forced to build in a location not suited to the type of nest of the species, birds almost invariably attempt to construct their regular nests. As in so many other cases, innate nest building does not function well in unusual situations. These nests are often so unsuitable to the abnormal location that they collapse, spill eggs, and result in other catastrophes. The bird will frequently build the same unsuccessful nest again and again. Nest building is synchronized with the development of eggs in the reproductive organs of the female.

Ceremonial offering of nest material also appears in many courtship displays. It may continue into the egg and incubation period, when it can have no practical value as far as actual nest construction is concerned. The well-known pebble-offering ceremony is a conspicuous and utilitarian part of penguin courtship. Like other display, nest-material offering has become so ritualized in many species that it usually consists of little more than "going through the motions." Doubtless it plays a similar part in the life of birds as other formalized behavior, like courtship feeding, and had its origins in activities that were once utilitarian, such as the pebble offering of the penguins.

Broodiness, or the drive causing a bird to sit on and warm the eggs, is brought on in part by the presence of eggs in the nest. But if herring gull eggs are placed in the nest of a gull that has not yet laid, and therefore has not progressed physiologically to the broody period, she will not brood — she will dine on them. The sight of eggs alone is not enough to stimulate broody behavior, which does not begin in most birds until egg laying is completed.

The completion of egg laying seems to be conveyed to birds in two different ways. Some species will not stop laying and brood until they *see* the number of eggs of their typical clutch in the nest. Swallows have been made to lay as many as fifty eggs by systematic nest robbing on the part of the observer. Flickers have produced as many as seventy under these circumstances. In contrast, some other species will lay their typical number and stop. Neither the addition nor subtraction of other eggs alters the number laid. The herring gull will usually lay three eggs and then stop regardless of the visual influence of the number of eggs actually in the nest. If all eggs are removed some time will elapse before more laying takes place. In species in this category the signal for cessation of laying and start of brooding is the physiological effect of laying a certain number of eggs. Broodiness in birds of the first category is brought on by the visual stimulus of the correct number of eggs in the nest. In either case, if all eggs are removed the bird will not brood an empty nest for long. However, many species will continue to brood completely inappropriate objects if these have been substituted.

It has been found in domestic hens and pigeons that the pituitary hormone prolactin stimulates broodiness. It is safe to assume that this is the case in other birds although experimental evidence is lacking. Probably the pituitary is stimulated to produce prolactin in some species by the visual impression of a certain number of eggs. The stimulation is activated in others by the physiological effect of a certain number of eggs having been laid.

From this and other examples above we begin to see that behavior patterns are the result of interrelated activities in which one phase leads to stimulation of or directly stimulates the next step in the cycle. The patterns appear to be complex to the point of incomprehensibility. The releasing mechanisms from within the bird's own body and from the activity or appearance of its mate or fellows are influenced by and interrelated to the environment and its stimuli. All work together to "guide" the bird to the proper innate activity at the proper time.

Hatching brings a change in behavior and a new stimuli to initiate it. The chicks must be fed, brooded, defended, and sheltered. That this change is also stimulated and timed, in part, by some internal factor is shown by the fact that birds will not accept a young bird or a hatching egg during the early part of the incubation period. But if these are offered near the end of this time the bird will accept them warmly even though her own eggs have several days to go before hatching. The passage of time approximating the incubation period of the species is part of the controlling factor. The final signal for changed behavior is the sight and sound of the young themselves.

The gaping of young is one of the stimuli that creates an ardent desire to feed them in the adults of many species. The young, in turn, are stimulated at a very early age to gape, by such signals as vibration of the nest and later by the sight and shape of the parent's head. Like other parts of birds which serve as sign stimuli, the mouths of nestlings are brightly colored and have great contrast.

As has been said before, behavior that takes place in the normal course of a bird's life functions so smoothly that it appears to be controlled by rational and purposeful thinking. Also, as before, it is only when a departure from normal is observed that the innate nature of these activities can be seen. The European cuckoo, like our cowbird, is parasitic. It lays its eggs entirely in the nests of other species of birds. Many of the young cuckoo's adaptations fit it to compete with the young of its foster parents with drastic success. In the first place, its incubation period is shorter and it hatches larger and stronger than the young of the victim species. Shortly after hatching, the young cuckoo boosts the eggs of the foster parents out of the nest. If the young have beat him to hatching by some chance, he treats them in the same impersonal manner. And, as if all this were not enough for dealing with the situation, the young cuckoo has a particularly large gape and brightly colored mouth and throat. When the parent comes to feed its own young, if any are left by this time, the super gaping of the baby cuckoo stimulates feeding so much more than the less spectacular gaping of the rightful offspring that the cuckoo is fed first and most. Also, the young may not have been completely ejected from the nest and may be lying about the rim. The parents do not save their own by pushing them back. They are allowed to starve while the cuckoo, flashing his brilliant gape, is stuffed with food. It is evident that these birds are not using reason concerning the situation. They are simply following unlearned inherited reactions that are activated by signs or internal or external stimuli, the innate releasing mechanisms. In the case of the cuckoo, a stronger releasing mechanism was provided by its brighter gape than the rightful young could manage. Therefore the super stimulus directed feeding behavior toward the cuckoo. Lorenz says that in a mixed aviary a baby cuckoo becomes a "sin." All the parent birds passionately indulge themselves by feeding it rather than their own young.

A brief account of Tinbergen's work with herring gull chicks will give further insight into the nature of innate behavior and the signs that stimulate it. This series of experiments also shows that innate releasing mechanisms work well enough for the survival of the species but are not always as efficient as is possible. In this case it was Dr. Tinbergen and not a cuckoo who did the improving.

As soon as it is dry and has become active after hatching, a herring gull chick pecks at the tip of the parent's bill. The bill is yellow and there is a bright red spot on the lower mandible. It is at this spot that the chick aims. Regurgitated food is held between the bill tips by the adult. In pecking at the red spot the chick gets

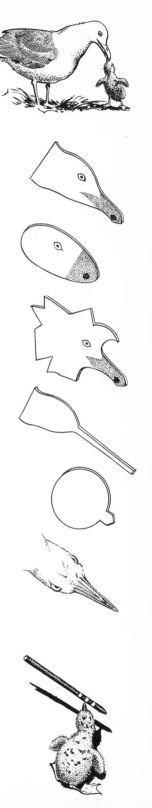

the food and eventually learns where its nourishment comes from. Dr. Tinbergen constructed many models of adult gull heads from flat cardboard. These were painted many different colors and contrasts. There were normal white heads with red-spotted yellow bills, models in which the color of the spot was varied, models where the contrast of the spot was changed from black to white, bill color was changed, the shape of the bill and head was distorted, a three-dimensional model was constructed and compared with flat models for effectiveness in getting pecking responses.

Sixteen thousand tests were made on newly hatched chicks who had never fed. The results showed that the red color of the spot and its contrast to the bill were the important factors. The color of the bill did not matter so long as it contrasted strongly with the red spot. The shape of the head was not in the least important, but the shape of the bill was. Since a chick generally sees its parent's bill for the first time from beneath, it appears as a long thin projection. The experiments showed that an extra-long thin bill got better responses than a normal one. Responses to the flat cardboard models were just as good as to the three-dimensional models and real gulls. Even bills with no heads were tried and worked as well as those with heads. Finally, with the facts at hand that contrast, red color, and long thin shape were the decisive factors, a super gull bill was constructed. It couldn't have looked less like the real thing. Three white rings were painted around the end of a thin red rod, providing elements of contrast, redness, and thinness to the greatest degree possible. The super gull bill proved far more effective in stimulating pecking in the chicks than the best dummy or an actual parent. Tinbergen has called this phenomenon "supernormal stimulus." In this case the supernormal stimulus was responded to by baby gulls. The supernormal stimulus provided by the baby cuckoo's bright gape affected adult birds.

Man has improved on nature by creating supernormal stimuli for the display characteristics of his own species (as the size and prosperity of our cosmetic, jewelry, and fancy-clothing industries attest).

Feeding often continues after the young birds have flown from the nest; but, as they mature, parental care ceases and the young are often driven from the feeding territory. The behavior of domestic hens in pecking and repulsing chicks whom they had tenderly fed and clucked over a few days before is well known. This sudden and seemingly cruel lack of solicitude is doubtless adaptive behavior causing wide dispersal, which prevents congestion, food shortage, and later excessive inbreeding.

As the breeding cycle ends, the hormonal stimuli that initiated this long and complex chain of events ceases and the bird resumes its daily self-maintenance of food getting, self-protection, and travel. Territorial behavior usually disappears, nesting colonies are abandoned in social species, and pairs break up among birds that do not mate for life. Fighting and threat are also largely discontinued. Fellows are either ignored in solitary species or tolerated in those that flock or congregate.

Social Behavior

SOCIAL BEHAVIOR exists when two or more animals aid each other in living. There is evidence that nearly all forms of life can and do, in one way or another, help each other. The sperm of the sea urchin *Arbacia* live longer in certain densities than when alone. The eggs of *Arbacia* develop faster in large groups than in small. Many protists live better and reproduce faster together than when alone. From these simple beginnings up through the evolutionary scale to the highly organized societies of man on one hand and insects on the other we find evidence that social cooperation is as important an instinctive drive as is that of competition.

In the so-called higher animals cooperation is more organized and complex than the mere grouping together of the simpler animals. But no real society can exist in a state of anarchy. From the rational, or at least rationalized, societies of man through almost all classes of vertebrate animals to the complex instinctively organized societies of insects, organization and law are necessary to make the group workable.

Painstaking work with flocks of domestic fowl has brought to light a good deal of the organization that keeps a flock of these birds in order. A group of hens that are strangers to each other will commence a series of fights, squabbles, and trials of strength to find out just who can lick or bluff whom. Gradually there emerges an order of dominance. Because this fighting consists largely of one bird pecking the other about the head and shoulders this social system has come to be called "peck order." In a flock that has lived together long enough for the peck order to become established there is a top bird who is boss. Under this bird is the second in command, who is pecked by the boss but pecks all the others; a third bird is pecked by the top two but pecks the rest; and so on down to the last bird, who pecks no one. The order is not always in such a straight line. For example, D may peck B but be pecked by A and C.

Flocks of roosters have more irregular organization. In mixed flocks each cock dominates all hens. Dominance of male over female seems necessary for successful and efficient

mating. Cocks who dominate other males have been proved to father more chicks in a flock than those lower in the male peck order. But hens of the lower orders are more successful mothers. High-ranking females are less likely to submit to the cocks. Thus successful maleness goes with aggressiveness and the resulting dominance. Successful femaleness is associated with mildness and submissiveness.

In flocks composed of young males the dominant ones will often attempt coition and tread the submissive males low in the peck order. In flocks of females the dominant birds take the male role toward the low-order hens. The injection of male sex hormones will cause a low-order female to revolt successfully and win higher rank but become less popular with the males.

The leaders of flocks are not necessarily males or even females highest in the peck order. Often some lowly member will take over when the group moves. Females are most often leaders of mixed flocks. Konrad Lorenz sees leadership as akin to social independence and not dominance. The lead bird is capable of independently striking out on its own, while the rest follow innately, maintaining flock unity. However, the leader never loses its dependence upon the flock. When it gets too far ahead it will turn back or stop and wait for its companions.

Social systems based on dominance also appear in wild birds, although they are not nearly so clear cut and simple. Among Lorenz's beloved jackdaws, who have lived for many years about the roofs and chimneys of his home in Austria, there was a definite and well-established peck order. But, differing from the chickens, jackdaws of high rank were very tolerant to those far beneath them. High-ranking birds regularly performed police action in breaking up squabbles among the lower orders by siding with the weaker bird. As most of these contentions were concerned with nest locations, the discipline protected the nesting of the humble and increased the breeding efficiency of the whole colony. Also, jackdaws pair more or less permanently. When males of high position mated with females low in the scale, the females at once assumed their husbands' rank.

There are other features of close cooperation among jackdaws. One evening, when returning from a swim, Dr. Lorenz went among his jackdaws forgetting that wet bathing trunks were in his pocket. Reacting suddenly as the dankness at last seeped through, he pulled out the black trunks "and the next moment was surrounded by a dense cloud of raging, rattling jackdaws, which hailed agonizing pecks upon my offending hand." Later other black fluttering objects, such as the paper strips from a camera's film pack, brought on this same violence. A featherless baby jackdaw could be picked up in perfect safety. The instant the growing black feathers burst the sheaths and the bird developed wandering habits that took it from the safety of the nest, handling it brought

bloody war, not only by its rightful parents but by any jackdaw. Anything black that appeared to move in the hand meant "jackdaw in the jaws of the enemy" and served as an innate releasing mechanism for cooperative jackdaw battle. This adaptation serves the direct purpose of occasionally rescuing an embattled bird and giving jackdaw predators a conditioned distaste for jackdaws in general, and also identifies jackdaw enemies to all adult birds as well as to members of the rising generation. At a single rattling cry young birds learn to recognize the particular individual it is directed toward, who from that time on is identified on sight as an enemy by the whole colony, whether the moving black object is still carried or not. This knowledge is thus taught to the next generation as they grow. Much the same mechanism of imparting predator identification exists among crows and other social species.

The advantages of a social system appear in greater stability of the flock as a functioning whole. In domestic flocks where order has become established, more eggs are laid, more chicks raised, and the birds eat more, are in better condition, and appear happier than in

flocks where social order has not become established. In any group of birds there is much more likely to be one who will spot danger and give warning. In food finding the flock instinct often leads the entire group to share the food found by one. Dense flying formations give protection against hawks, which are vulnerable to collision unless they strike a single bird accurately with their talons. The *V* formation of geese and others makes flying aerodynamically easier for all but the leader, who changes place with a follower quite often. Other species in addition to jackdaws and crows carry out cooperative attacks on predators, as anyone who has strolled through a colony of breeding gulls well knows.

undisturbed

Flock of starlings under attack by peregrine falcon
(after Tinbergen)

Colonial nesters show definite tendencies to breed and raise young more efficiently when their colonies have reached a certain size. Very small groups, the result of partial extinction or the formation of new colonies, breed late and less efficiently and often fail to breed successfully at all. Perhaps some form of sympathetic induction stimulates large colonies to perform the steps of the reproductive pattern better. This factor, in addition to the phenomenon of genetic drift, may very well be the prime cause for the sudden extinction of populations of birds that have already become dangerously reduced. In the fall of 1960 there were only six captive and thirty-six wild whooping cranes in existence. It would not take much of an unfavorable reproductive balance to finish this species forever.

Birds breeding in colonies exhibit territorial behavior of much the same sort as birds breeding in solitary pairs. Colonial territories have nothing to do with food supply, because the adult birds feed away from the nesting area. So defense is confined to the nest and a rather small space around it. Peck order does not usually affect territorial disputes — each bird tends to be dominant in its own area. But birds low in the peck order may not be able to hold as large an area about the nest or stake a claim to as favorable a spot or hole as do birds higher up. In many species of ground-nesters territorial behavior creates an optimum distribution of nests. In gulls the territory size separates individual nests so that they do not form too dense and easily available a cafeteria for predators but still retain the advantages that proximity gives these birds. Among many penguin species territory consists of the area around each nest that will just allow one brooding bird to peck its neighbor. In other words, the nests are packed as closely as possible in an island or arctic environment of few predators.

Migration

OF ALL the things birds do that so appeal to humans, the most romantic is the long, long trip many species make twice every year. All of us thrill to see the ducks go north or to hear the *clang* of Canada geese in the spring skies. Young or old, we tingle a little and are filled with a strange yearning to follow these great birds as they go northward to the wild land where spring comes with a tumbling rush. In the autumn when the waterfowl go south again and the sky is filled with runes of other birds, we wonder about and envy them the green marshes, dark still jungle rivers, and all the warm exotic places they are headed for. As the bright bits of life leave our fields and gardens almost unnoticed to disappear into the distances of continents, we wish them well. The gray months of winter seem to wait for the days that will bring the birds back to fill the mornings with sound and movement. Perhaps the almost unfelt emotions that rise when we see the birds migrate are faint echoes of unused instincts left from a time when men also moved with the seasons.

The migratory journeys are not always long north and south movements. They may be short trips from a cold mountain slope to its warm valley. They may be east-west movements in search of favorable food supply. At the other extreme, there are trips like that of the arctic tern, who yearly travels from above the Arctic Circle to antarctic regions— 11,000 miles one way.

Although migration is synchronized with the breeding cycle, the basic cause for it is food. Birds can stand low temperatures if they are well nourished, but in the scarcity of the northern winter only a few — those adapted to use what small supply there is — can stay behind. So most species winter in warm lands. Then the coming of spring brings the need to reproduce. Egg production and fast-growing young demand plentiful supplies of rich food close at hand and longer hours of daylight in which to find it. Many birds leave the crowded tropics to go north when the warmth of the northward-moving sun brings arctic and temperate lands to life again.

In some species northerly-breeding races migrate, while those breeding farther south are resident all year round. In many intermediate areas, some of a species move out with winter and others stay behind. Many birds leave the breeding grounds long before winter comes, when supplies are still plentiful. Some birds, called weather migrants, merely move with favorable conditions. Extra-severe winters cause them to leave an area in which they would normally stay. Mild

weather may find them farther north than cus-
tomary. Weather migration may well represent
a stage that was the beginning of typical migratory behavior millions of years ago. But true
migration is an inherited innate behavior pattern. The conditions that created it as an
adaptation favorable to the species performing
it originally are not necessarily the conditions
that prevail today.

The marking of birds — and thus the indi-
vidualizing of them — with numbered leg bands
has established many facts about migration.
Definite migration routes tend to be used year
after year by the same birds and their descend-
ants. These are not narrow roadlike paths but
more or less broad geographical areas that include breeding and wintering grounds. The
areas, called flyways, can be mapped more and
more accurately as returns from banded birds
accumulate over the years. Recent information
tends to indicate that flyway systems are not as
consistent and well defined as formerly supposed, but the conception is valid enough to
serve many useful purposes in dealing with
problems of migration, especially in the management of migratory game species.

The use of a particular flyway by populations
or races of a species, or sometimes an entire
species, is hereditary. If trapped in one route
and moved to an entirely different one, some
will return to the original flyway before contin-

uing migration. Others may migrate by leaving the new location in a direction parallel to that which they would have
followed in the old, regardless of whether this leads them to a
favorable breeding or wintering area or not. The use of hereditary paths is so consistent that individual birds have been
trapped by banders year after year in the same traps at nearly
the same date. Also, birds reappear at the same nesting
ground and wintering area year after year with remarkable
faithfulness. Young birds come back to the vicinity of their
birth or, after the wandering that takes place when they separate from their parents, to the location from which they
departed the previous fall.

Although the rates of migratory trips are of little value in
indicating the absolute speed of bird flight, banding records
do show how fast the total trip or fractions of it are made.
The southward flight is often a leisurely journey made up of
resting and feeding stopovers alternating with flights. The
spring trip tends to be faster. Many species show signs of
frantic haste as they push northward on the very edge of
spring. Small birds can and have traveled from one to 200
miles a day but, as a rule, do not cover more than 50 or 60
miles. Larger birds can travel farther. A blue-winged teal
was banded in Minnesota and recovered ten days later in
Colombia, South America, 3000 miles away. A lesser yellowlegs is known to have averaged 316 miles a day. But these are
record performances and do not necessarily apply to typical
rates of travel.

Certain species do regularly perform tremendous feats of
nonstop long-distance flying. The American golden plover
probably reaches winter quarters in South America by flying
over water from Labrador and Nova Scotia, 2400 miles. A
subspecies, the Pacific golden plover, migrates from Alaska

to Hawaii, almost 3000 miles, entirely over open water.

The "why" of migration seems obviously based on food supply and length of daylight during the breeding period and the records of when and where are vast and accurate. Nevertheless, the two most basic questions concerning it have been only partly answered. First — just what stimulus causes a bird, warm and plentifully supplied with food, to go northward in the spring? After breeding is over, what causes it to

go south often long before cold weather comes? What is the timing device used to tell a bird when to come and go? How does it work? The second question — how do these small creatures do it? How do they find their way over the vast reaches of land and water that many of them cover?

The first good hint to the answer to question one came with the pioneer experiments that the late William Rowan first reported in 1925. During the Canadian winter in an outdoor aviary slate-colored juncos were exposed to an artificially increased length of daylight exactly corresponding to the increase that would normally take place in the spring. As controls, other juncos were kept nearby under the same conditions but without the extra light. The gonads, or sexual organs, of the first group gradually enlarged just as would be normal in the spring. The gonads of the second group re-

mained inactive. When released most of the sexually activated birds disappeared (migrated?), and the controls re-
mained in the vicinity. Later experiments with other species
have given similar results.

Since Rowan's first experiments a great deal of attention
has been given to the physiological condition of birds readied
for migration by natural as well as artificial means. Increase
of stored energy such as fat, the speed up of pituitary and
thyroid activity, the general restlessness many species show,
particularly at night, and other evidences of "lift" of metabolic rates have been studied in many different species. When
all the evidence (far too scanty yet to base definite conclu-
sions upon) is viewed as a whole, it is possible to form a reasonable hypothesis that the increasing length of daylight
during the spring stimulates the pituitary gland to release
certain hormones. These stimulate the system directly or
affect other endocrines like those of the thyroid and the endocrines of the gonads, which in turn release their hormonal
products and put the bird in "condition" to migrate and
breed. Probably temperature changes and favorable traveling conditions trigger the beginning of the trip, once the bird
has achieved this condition. There is evidence that rising
temperatures in spring, wind direction, and the large moving
masses of air called "fronts" correlate significantly with mass
movements of birds even to temporarily reversing the direction of migration. Instinctive recognition of the position of
the sun or stars (or both) in the sky at certain periods of the
year may well be one of the factors that wakes the ancient
urge to migrate.

Environmental and physiological stimuli for the autumn
trip are an even more speculative matter. Many birds leave
for wintering areas long before there is any need to do so.

The windup of reproductive tasks and molting does relieve birds of these exceptionally heavy demands upon their energy and may result in a metabolic balance on the plus side for a short time. The gonads regress at this time but the *lessening* period of daily light may have an equally profound effect upon the pituitary and its many products. It is not necessarily more light that stimulates this gland, but a *change* in the light period. Emperor penguins breed during the antarctic winter. They migrate southward just at the time the southern days are getting shorter, and breed in total darkness. Brook trout come into spawning condition in the autumn and have been made to spawn early by artificially *decreasing* the length of daylight. These facts, plus the knowledge that birds, and many other animals, have a slight recurrence of secondary sexual activity in the fall — like song and territorial behavior — make it reasonable to suppose that decreasing light may be responsible for some inner change that stimulates the bird to make the southern trip.

Of course, the pituitary hypothesis, as related to the changing length of daylight, can apply only to birds who migrate from areas not on or near the equator. The change of photoperiod (length of daylight) here is so imperceptible as to appear nonexistent for practical purposes. This complicates matters, because some species remain south to breed, both near and far from the equator, and some migrate from both areas.

Inconsistencies resulting from accurate but conflicting findings of many workers have led to confusion and disagreement about every phase of bird migration. Man's desire to put all causes for a phenomenon into one single neat package of simplicity and universality has been a particular hindrance to getting at a comprehension of the mysteries of migration. Actually, birds are natural objects for the development of migratory behavior. Flight, the strong tendency to inherit instinctive behavior patterns, and their tremendous energy especially fit them for this way of life. If true migration can be performed by such diverse animals as butterflies, seals, fish, and bats, it is almost certain that such behavior could have come about independently in separate hereditary lines of birds. If so, it is probable that various groups of birds have become adapted to a migratory way of life in different ways. However, it is not strange that light seems to figure so strongly, not only in migratory behavior but in many other processes of life, among many widely separate organisms such as insects and plants. Light, or its absence, is one of the most prominent features of the environment. It is to be expected that as organisms evolved they became adapted to use changes in light as a stimulus for many of their reactions.

How birds know where to go and where they are is even more of a puzzle. Without question a good deal of avian navigation is performed by following such learned features of the landscape as rivers, coastlines, or valleys. Improvement in the homing performances of pigeons that have been trained by repeatedly releasing them at greater distances from the home loft must be the result of learning. Many species have been released over strange territory and followed by airplane. In finding their way home they have performed a wandering flight pattern that has been visualized as consisting of irregular but definite patterns of search that continue until recognizable landmarks, learned or innately known, or other clues are found.

Only while traveling in fog or under heavy overcast do birds seem to get lost. They are able to correct their direction as soon as the weather clears again. Disasters do occur, however. There are endless records of "wrecks" of birds appearing at entirely wrong places on land, islands, or ships at sea, exhausted and badly off the regular course of their species. Even sea birds are often confused during fogs and come to land or raft on the water in large flocks. Perhaps bird migration is not as infallible as we have become accustomed to think it. We shall never forget the wild, searching cries of a

huge flock of Canada geese that almost scraped the chimney on our hilltop house as they circled in a pea-soup fog.

But this is not the whole story of bird navigation. Many young birds who have never migrated make the autumn trip south and the spring trip north again alone and without the possibility of help from experienced adults. A few further examples of some actual feats of navigation will show beyond a doubt that a great many birds must possess some sort of compass. Noddy and sooty terns, transported from nesting grounds on the Dry Tortugas Islands in the Gulf of Mexico and released hundreds of miles away over unmarked ocean in a strange area, showed a remarkable percentage of return. Manx shearwaters were shipped from Skokholm, Wales, to Venice by air and released. The trip back over unfamiliar territory was 900 miles by land and 3000 by the shortest sea route. One of the birds made it home in two weeks. Another Skokholm shearwater, sent to Boston by air, got home to its nest burrow 3000 miles away in twelve and a half days. Swallows from Bremen, Germany, shipped to England returned in as little as four days. And so on through innumerable examples of remarkable navigational ability.

This apparent ability to navigate accurately by some means strange to any perceptions we recognize in ourselves has led to considerable speculation, some of which is quite imaginative. Ideas have included supposed sensitivity to the magnetic field of the earth, to various effects and forces caused by the rotation of the earth, and even extra visual sensitivity to infrared light — which birds do not have — as a means of orientation. All these theories require the ability to detect forces so slight as probably to be smothered by more ordinary and unavoidable forces of the environment. Even under conditions perfect for their detection, ability to perceive such forces would require organs of a degree of sensitivity that does not seem possible for any living creature. However, scientific objectivity does not allow any theory to be completely ruled out until it has been actually disproved.

Important and significant experiments have been made by the late Gustav Kramer that do shed light on the mystery of bird navigation. In Germany, Kramer confined starlings in a circular aviary from which only the overhead sky was visible. When food was consistently placed in the same location the birds easily found it at any time of day. But when the sky was heavily overcast they flew at random — in all directions — when looking for the food. In other words, they were lost. During the migratory season many captive birds exhibit restlessness and repeatedly fly and orient themselves in the direction they would normally take when freely traveling. Kramer confined young starlings in migratory condition in a large covered cage with a window in each of its six sides. When he placed mirrors at these six windows in such a way that all light entering the enclosure was deflected by 90 degrees, the flight of the starlings was also deflected by exactly 90 degrees.

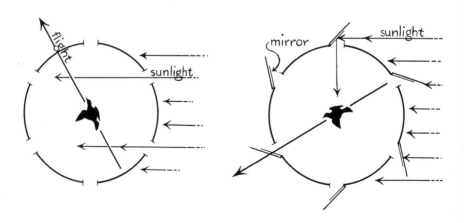

On sunny days or under a light overcast the birds could orient themselves at any time of day. Under a heavy overcast they again completely lost their sense of direction. The birds must have been directing themselves in reference to the position of the sun in the sky. As the sun moves, of course, this means of navigation not only would require the ability to use the light of the sun as a compass, but would also require a sense of time of day in relation to its position. It was also found that birds would direct themselves in a completely covered aviary by means of a single bright light that served as a substitute sun.

Exciting new experiments by E. G. F. Sauer, also in Germany, if verified by further work, will just about complete the explanation of the external means of bird navigation. During the restlessness that occurs throughout migratory periods in many night-migrating species, Sauer's captive warblers always pointed in a certain geographical direction "like the needle of a compass." This direction always coincided with the direction their flight would have taken if they had been freely migrating. When the perches in cages permitting only a view of the overhead night sky were turned, the birds always resumed the migratory direction characteristic of their species. Sauer then placed test birds in a planetarium. When the dome was illuminated with diffuse light and showed no stars, the birds could not orient themselves, but when this artificial sky was made to match the natural starry sky, the birds promptly oriented again. When the "sky" was shifted the birds made the correct adjustment in their position. A lesser whitethroat exposed to a sky five hours early for the time of day (correct for a position 77 degrees longitude eastward at that particular time) was confused for only about a minute. Then it suddenly turned and flew to the westward,

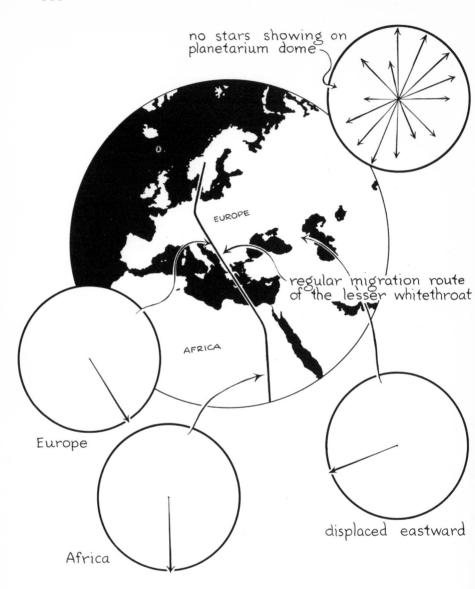

no stars showing on planetarium dome

regular migration route of the lesser whitethroat

EUROPE

AFRICA

Europe

Africa

displaced eastward

Principal directions of flight taken under planetarium dome when star patterns for positions indicated on map were simulated toward the correct migration route in Germany! These birds not only can recognize and steer themselves by means of the constellations in the sky but have a built-in clock that tells them the correct sky for the time of day and year.

These remarkable experiments, still going on, were conducted with birds that had been raised entirely in cages and never migrated at all as well as with older birds that had migrated, thus demonstrating that the ability to navigate by the recognition of the pattern of the stars may be an inherited instinct.

We now know that some birds, at least, can steer themselves by the stars or sun night or day over the distant reaches of their migratory paths. The Manx shearwater, mentioned earlier, which returned to its nest in Skokholm from Boston in twelve and one-half days, must have been able to find its way home over the unrecognizable reaches of the ocean by celestial navigation! At home under skies its ancestors had

become innately adapted to recognize, it could "feel right" in the place on earth that was right for *it* at that time of day and year.

Primitive people have always used the sun and stars to orient their position. Many humans seem to have a better sense of direction than others. Perhaps this ability is also innate. Remarkable feats of land and sea navigation without instruments are recorded. Knowledge of astronomy and aid of navigational devices have made man a navigator vastly superior to any animal. Perhaps he has become so superior that ancient innate ability has been obscured. Science may have now quite thoroughly answered the question of how birds navigate as far as external means are concerned. But, as is usual in living things, these answers are only the beginning. The whole "how"—how these supersensitive navigational devices function as part of the incredible complexity of the living nervous system—will answer many fundamental questions about birds, and about men.

3

Anatomy and Physiology

Skin and Feathers

PICK UP the next flight feather you see. Feel its lightness; test its strength where rigidity is needed to support the stresses of flight, and its suppleness where flexibility allows the constant change of shape and function which makes possible the controlled, split-second agility of bird flight. Run your finger along the vane and watch the ripple of the interlocked surface as it gives to your touch. Examining this marvel under a microscope or a good magnifying glass is an exciting experience for anyone.

The basal part of a feather is the quill, or calamus. At its tip is a small hole, the inferior umbilicus, through which blood passed during the development of the feather. The material that was necessary for the feather's growth can be

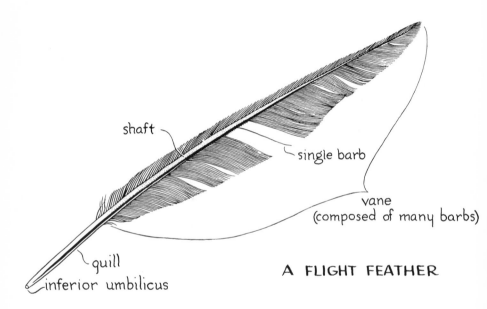

shaft

single barb

vane
(composed of many barbs)

quill

inferior umbilicus

A FLIGHT FEATHER

seen as dried remains in the hollow quill. On the underside of the quill at its upper limit is another small hole, the superior umbilicus. Near this point there often grows a tuft of down or an extra feather, called an aftershaft. It is usually small but is as big as the contour feather itself in some feathers of some species. The quill of the main feather is held in the feather follicle, a pit sinking deep into the skin.

The solid shaft, or rachis, continues the center line of the quill up into the exposed part of the feather. From either side

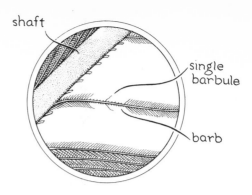

of this shaft the barbs project diagonally outward. From the barbs the barbules project in a similar manner, making each barb seem like a tiny feather in itself. Barbules are too small to be seen by the naked eye, and they in turn bear even smaller projections, called barbicels. Many of the barbicels possess tiny hooklets, the hamuli, which catch over the barbules above them and hold the entire vane together in a continuous, flexible, and surprisingly strong sheet. When the vane is parted by accident or ordinary wear and tear, the barbules become rehooked either automatically or during preening and the feather is whole again. This structure is so efficient and so similar in birds that barbs of widely unrelated species can be smoothly united by placing them side by side and stroking with the fingers. This marrying of feathers of different species is often done in making elaborate flies for fishing.

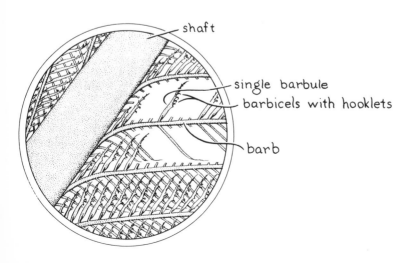

We have been describing the structure of a typical contour feather. The flight feathers of the wing (remiges), those of the tail (rectrices), along with the other more or less solidly vaned covering feathers are called contour feathers.

The bristles growing about the mouths, nostrils, and eyes of many birds are modified contour feathers. Bristles about the mouth, as in

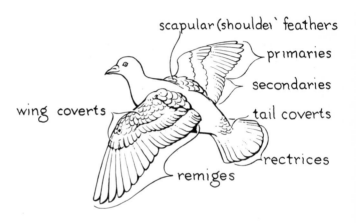

scapular (shoulder) feathers
primaries
secondaries
wing coverts
tail coverts
rectrices
remiges

the whip-poor-will, aid in catching insects while in flight. Bristles about nostrils and eyes serve to protect these organs from foreign particles in the air, and may also be sensory.

A second type of feather is the down that usually underlies the contour feathers. It is the warm and often waterproof insulating material that plays so important a part in making the high temperature of birds possible. The structure of down is simpler than that of contour feathers. True down feathers have little or no

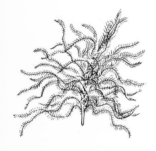

DOWN FEATHER

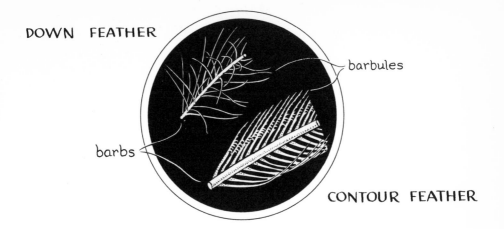

DOWN FEATHER

barbules

barbs

CONTOUR FEATHER

shaft. The barbs spring directly from the quill where it emerges from the body. Down feathers are characterized by the absence of interlocking devices on the barbs, which are therefore not hooked together to form a vane. Thus the long, fluffy barbs mix and interweave with each other and those of neighboring down feathers to form a dense air-filled insulating mat beneath the shingled surface of the contour feathers. Men have not yet been able to find or make a better material for warm sleeping bags or quilted clothing than the down of the eider duck.

Semiplumes are downy feathers with the shaft developed to varying degrees. Authorities do not all agree as to exactly what constitutes a semiplume. But, like down, semiplumes have no hooking devices and thus no firm vanes. They also serve as insulating layers and for buoyancy, as well as serving to form a flexible feather covering where moving parts preclude stiffer plumage.

A third type of feather is the hair feather, or filoplume. This is a simple, tiny, hairlike shaft that may or may not have a tuft of finer filaments at the tip. The exact function of filoplumes is not known.

Like the hair, hoofs, claws, nails, and true horns of mam-

FILOPLUME

mals and the scales of reptiles, feathers are special cornified growths of the epidermis and are a part of the skin. Skin has two layers: the outer, or epidermis; and the inner layer, the dermis. The epidermis is composed of several cell layers. The outermost of these consists of flat, hard, lifeless cells in which a material called keratin is present. This layer is relatively hard, or cornified, and is constantly replaced, as it is worn off by the wear and tear of life, by new layers, which grow from beneath.

The beginning of feather growth takes place while the bird is still in the egg. A feather papilla, or bud, is first formed and then sinks into a pit, the feather follicle. The papilla consists of mesodermal pulp with its blood vessels and is covered by epidermis. It begins to protrude outward as the future feather develops. It thus becomes a cone with a nourishing pulp-filled center and an epidermal surface. The outermost cells of the epidermis become a horny cover, a protecting sheath that elongates as the feather forms within it. The innermost epidermal cells, nourished by the blood vessels in the pulp, form the feather itself. In a down feather longitudinal ridges grow out from a collar around the base to become the barbs. Upon completion of growth, the nutritive pulp is reabsorbed, the horny sheath breaks open, and the downy filaments are released.

Development of a contour feather is a bit more complicated but basically similar to that

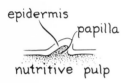

epidermis
papilla
nutritive pulp

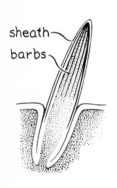

sheath
barbs

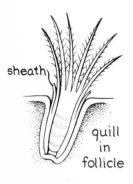

sheath
quill
in
follicle

**DOWN-FEATHER
DEVELOPMENT**

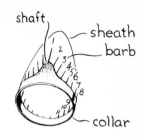

shaft sheath barb collar

of a down feather. Growth begins in the same way but the basal collar puts forth an especially heavy upgrowth, which becomes the shaft. This pulls the barbs, continually forming on the collar, along with it as it grows. In time the barbules with their barbicels grow out from the barbs. When the feather matures, nutritive material is no longer needed; the sheath splits and falls away or is removed by preening, and the vane unrolls. The new feather is complete.

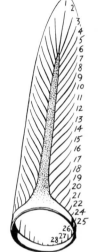

GROWTH OF CONTOUR FEATHER

There is a series of feather coats during the time of a bird's growth. At birth, or soon afterward, the young bird is covered with a coat of down. This is followed by one or more sets of juvenile feathers. The first of these push out the baby down feathers, which remain attached to their tips for a time and often give the youngster that scraggly adolescent appearance. Adult feathers follow in turn.

Grown birds also change their feathers, or molt, periodically to renew worn plumes or to assume the special breeding plumage displayed in the courtship of many groups. Molts usually

take place after the breeding season, before it, or both times. Consequently they are called post- and prenuptial molts. Molting is generally slow and continuous. In most groups of birds the feathers are not all shed from one area at the same time and the bird is not handicapped by the loss of too many feathers at once. The remiges and rectrices — flight feathers of the wing and tail — are often shed in single pairs, one from the right and one from the left side, and this preserves aerodynamic balance. There are special exceptions to the above. For example, ducks and geese lose all their flight feathers at one time in their postnuptial molt. During the resulting flightless period the males, in brightly colored species, molt into a coat of drab feathers very similar to those of the female. They become shy and secretive. The inconspicuous color, called eclipse plumage, and the changed behavior protect the birds during a time when they have lost one of their principal defenses. The eclipse usually lasts for about a month or two and can be compared to the dull-colored winter feathers in males of many other groups.

The replacement of feathers continues throughout the life of the bird. The papilla in each follicle is permanent. A new feather grows from it whenever molt or accidental loss makes replacement necessary. This is why the flight feathers of captive birds are clipped and not plucked. Plucking a feather from a living bird results in the immediate growth of a replacement.

Contour feathers do not grow evenly over the bodies of

most birds. They originate in definite areas (feather tracts), the pterylae. The areas from which feathers do not grow (apteria) cannot be seen casually because overlapping feathers from the pterylae cover them. This growth pattern of feathers is called pterylosis. The arrangement differs between groups of birds and may serve as a clue to the degree of relationship between them.

Some species change the appearance of parts of their plumage without molting. The little black bib of the male house sparrow is really present all during the winter, but it does not show until by mating time the light-colored tips have worn off and exposed the black.

Feathers are such excellent insulators that they could keep much of the bird's body heat from the eggs during incubation. Many birds have developed brood spots, areas on the breast and belly from which feathers molt at the proper time. Also, the bare skin of the brood spot is warmer than normal at this time. Local blood vessels increase in size and the area becomes red and inflamed. The absence of feathers allows this extra heat to get to the developing eggs. The number of brood spots varies in different groups of birds. Most songbirds, pigeons, grebes, and birds of prey have but one. Gulls and the related waders have three. In species in which the assistance from the male in brooding is anything more than a gesture he also develops brood spots.

ventral

dorsal

PTERYLOSIS

The attractive and often sensational colors of birds come from two main sources, pigment colors and structural colors. In birds the principal pigments are melanins and carotenoids. The melanins range from blacks and browns to light tans. They are the most common bird pigments and are synthesized by the bird itself. The carotenoid (lipochrome) pigments generally produce yellow, orange, and red. These are taken in with the food and, although they may be modified, are usually deposited directly in the skin or feathers with little or no chemical change. The herring gull's bright yellow bill with its red spot and the flamingo's rosy plumage are the result of carotenoid pigmentation.

Structural colors are caused by the microscopic surface structure of the feathers. This reflects various portions of the spectrum and overlies pigment layers. Blue, for instance, is not a pigment at all; it is caused as the surface structure of the barbs reflects blue light and allows the rest of the light to pass through and be absorbed by the dark melanin layer beneath. Green in some few cases (touracos) is an actual pigment. However, in most birds it is produced in a way similar to blue, except that the reflecting structure of the barb may be pigmented with melanin for olive greens or yellow carotenoids for brighter greens. White is produced by the reflection of almost all light.

Microscopic laminations in the structure of the barbules cause the reflection of light which gives the handsome iridescence to the head of the mallard drake, the peacock, and hummingbirds, among many others. This structure also has pigmented layers beneath it which modify the wave lengths of the reflected light.

The colors of birds have several functions. Cryptic, or concealing, coloration is common. This may break up the outline of a bird, obliterate its form as overhead light strikes dark topsides and leaves light undersides in shadow, or imitate the colors and forms of surroundings. Penguins are an example of how delicately balanced this type of cryptic coloration may be. When in the sea they swim in a horizontal position, dark backs uppermost. Even the soles of their feet, also uppermost when swimming, are black. In this they strikingly resemble the protective coloration of most fish, whales, and other water animals. On the land penguins stand upright and the cryptic nature of their coloration vanishes. However, when penguins evolved, adult birds had no natural enemies on *land* and their conspicuous black and white plumage was not detrimental but advantageous in social birds. Cryptic coloration may match colors and imitate shapes in the habitat, as shown in birds with broken, mottled plumage colors. Often both of the above types of camouflage are combined.

As we know, color also serves for communication between individuals of a species. It may repel rivals, attract and stimulate the opposite sex, stimulate flocking and following, and act

ON LAND

above

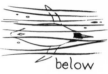

below

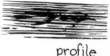

profile

IN WATER

as a warning signal. Gorgeous, subtle, immaculate, suave —
whatever adjective you may use, birds possess color patterns
as beautiful as those of any form of life.

Bird skin is light in weight, thin, and loose. Skin glands
are rare in birds. However, in most birds there is a large oil
gland located over the base of the tail. It secretes the oil that
is picked up by the bird's bill while preening and is worked
into the plumage as dressing and waterproofing material.

The mouth, gullet, stomach, intestines, and other internal
surfaces are protected by a mucous membrane that is continuous with the outside covering of skin. This sheet protects
delicate parts against mechanical damage, prevents excessive
loss of water from the body by evaporation, and is a barrier
against bacterial, chemical, and physical agents from both
the inside and outside surroundings.

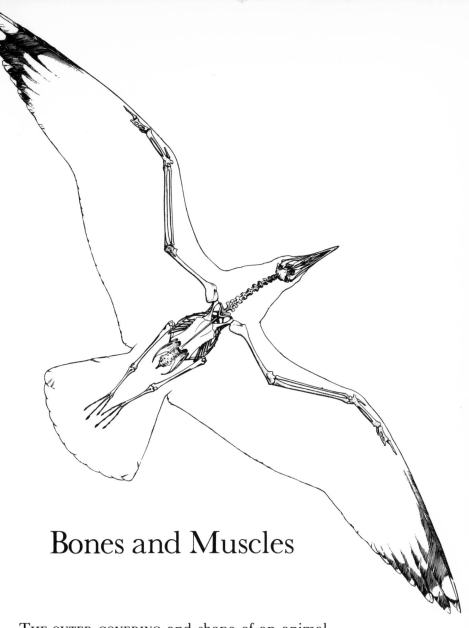

Bones and Muscles

THE OUTER COVERING and shape of an animal are often misleading. Until quite recently, for instance, men thought that whales were fish. They looked and acted like fish. One quick comparison of the whale's skeleton with those

of other animals would have told any intelligent person, *if he had compared*, that here was a creature related to a walking, land-dwelling animal. Inside the forefin are the bones of an arm, a wrist, and hand, changed a good deal to serve the needs of swimming but far more like those of a land animal than of any fish. Even the seven mammal-type vertebrae that make up the necks of a giraffe or a man appear in the apparently neckless whale. They are much compressed, to be sure, but yet are there.

The skeletal differences between the various groups of birds are never as great as they are among mammals. Nevertheless, they can be very revealing concerning the problems of bird relationship. Long ago penguins also had their turn at being thought of as fish, or as representing a halfway point between fish and birds. But the bones of their feathered forelimbs — flippers — are unmistakably those of a slightly modified bird wing. This and other evidence leaves no doubt whatever that they are descended from some long-ago group of flying water birds.

In addition to supplying a tremendous amount of information about the relationship and descent of birds, knowledge of the framework we call the skeleton is tremendously important in understanding how birds go about the business of being birds — how they move, defend themselves, get food. In addition to these active functions the skeleton also serves the passive purposes of housing and protecting the brain, nerve cord, digestive system, and other delicate parts that provide the energy and coordination to power and direct the bird's activity. The skeleton also provides places of attachment for a good many of the muscles.

The skeleton and muscles of birds are greatly changed from those of the primitive amphibian ancestors of the reptiles that in turn evolved into the two great classes of mammals and birds. Most of these changes are directly related to the average bird's way of getting about, flying, and, to a lesser degree, walking on two legs. Many of the bird's bones have become hollow, light, and air-filled. They have also become fused to such a great extent that the entire skeleton is much simplified as far as the number of actually moving, working parts is concerned. The bird skeleton consists, basically, of a few tubular struts and long slender limb bones, supporting and supported by thin bony plates that are strong because of their shape and not their weight or thickness. Many of the bones massive in appearance have a porous construction and are light in weight. The hollow wing bones of larger birds often are braced internally, as is the hollow wing of an airplane or the light stem and leaves of such plants as the cattail. Large heavy muscles are placed low and those of the extremities are small or may be completely absent, keeping the center of gravity low and central.

The forelimbs of birds are used almost entirely for flying. This may not seem to be a statement of any very startling subtlety. But this fact has a great deal to do with the shape and function of many other parts of the bird. The jaws must take the place of hands or forepaws. Birds not only catch and handle their food but care for plumage, build nests, care for young, defend themselves, and display with their beaks. To provide the necessary mobility of the head when the beak is used for these purposes the bird neck is long, strong, and flexible. The skull is light with very strong jaws, particularly in those birds that crack hard seeds or use the beak to kill or tear large prey or food into pieces small enough to swallow. The horny beak itself is of cornified epidermis and, so, technically should have been considered in the previous chapter. However, it is so much a part of the skull in function that we would be sacrificing meaning for the sake of order not to mention it here.

The beak is quite flexible and has sensory nerve endings and organs of taste in most groups of birds. Birds can perform feats of dexterity with the beak which appear impossible for such a seemingly hard and insensible organ. Once food is in the mouth they seldom drop it, even when it is of the slippery, wiggly variety. Birds can pick up, eject, juggle, and revolve very small particles. The ability of terns to manipulate small fish while in flight is well known. Many birds toss food nonchalantly into the air and catch it again to get it into a better position for swallowing. For instance, downing a finny fish demands a head-first technique.

Because birds' bills are so important in these operations, their shapes are myriad and have many special features to aid in various jobs. But in keeping with the necessity for the ultimate in lightness for a flying animal, no living birds have teeth. Along the edges of each mandible and on the tongue of the mallard and other ducks are rows of horny ridges (lamellae) which act like a sieve in straining small particles of food from soft mud or water. Our tame mallards actually prefer to have their grain thrown into the water so that they can sieve it out rather than pick it up from dry land or out of

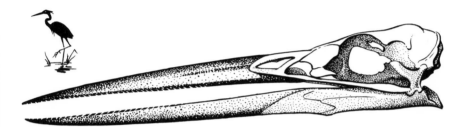

a dish in the seemingly easier methods. The beak of the great blue heron has backward-pointing slits along its edges. Fishy prey can slide in between this two-pronged animated spear but not out again. Different groups of birds have other adaptations for special uses in what seems like an almost endless array.

In response to the need for lightness, dexterity, and strength, the forces of evolution have created such an elegant structure in the bird's skull that we are going to take the risk of boring the reader with a rather detailed description. Each ridge, bump, or hollow for the attachment of muscles, each tiny opening for nerve or blood vessel, each moving joint, each stiff fused part has its exact and vital function. Many of these are beyond the scope of this book.

The skull is composed of more bones than would at first be

imagined. Most are indivisibly united in the adult bird. They can be seen clearly only in the very young. The skull of a young chicken when cleaned and boiled for a short time, can be separated into a handful of small delicate bones. We did just this with the head of a fryer, obtained from our butcher, to get the separate bones pictured on pages 130 and 133. For the most part these can be matched bone for bone and name for name with those of any higher backboned animal — including those of the human skull.

The bird skull has a light, strong, rounded brain case. It is notable for its huge eye sockets, or orbits, separated by a very thin, partially membranous, interorbital septum ("between the eye partition"; scientific language is usually simple enough and its Latin base is understood internationally). The ear cavity lies just behind the hinge of the jaw. The tympanic membrane, or eardrum, is stretched across its opening. Attached to the inner surface of this membrane is the columella, consisting of cartilage and the tiny stapes. Chapter 18 gives details on the function of this and the rest of the ear. At the base of the skull is the smooth, single, ball-bearing-like occipital condyle, which fits the socket of the first vertebra of the neck, the atlas, and forms a very flexible joint. Above and behind the occipital condyle is the foramen magnum (large hole), the opening for the spinal cord.

If the illustrations on pages 130 and 133 are followed as we "build" a bird's skull it will be quite easy to trace the interacting function of most of the skull's intricate bones.

The upper beak is formed by the large premaxilla. This is covered by the horny bill in birds but holds the upper front teeth in most other vertebrates. The large nostril opening is formed by the premaxilla as it unites with the nasal bones, one on each side of the skull. The rear, or posterior, ends of

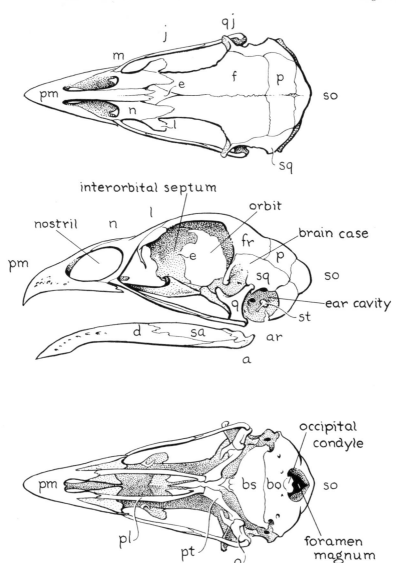

CHICKEN SKULL (actual size)
See following pages for explanation of abbreviations

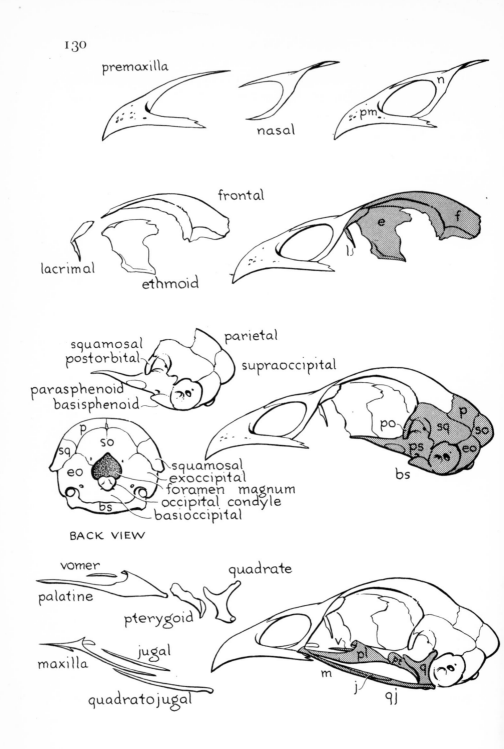

premaxilla

nasal

n

pm

frontal

lacrimal

ethmoid

e

f

squamosal
postorbital
parasphenoid
basisphenoid

parietal

supraoccipital

po

p

sq

so

ps

eo

p

so

sq

eo

squamosal
exoccipital
foramen magnum
occipital condyle
basioccipital

bs

bs

BACK VIEW

vomer

palatine

pterygoid

maxilla

jugal

quadratojugal

quadrate

v

pl

pt

q

m

j

qj

these overlap the frontal and ethmoid bones. Depending upon the adaptations of the bird, this joint is either rigid or surprisingly flexible. In birds like the rose-breasted grosbeak, whose bill is a heavy seed-cracking apparatus, the posterior ends of the nasal bones are thickened and expanded where they meet the frontals. In the great horned owl, which stabs downward with its hooked beak, the frontals are thickened and overlap the ends of the premaxilla and nasals, forming a groove into which these firmly fit. Other birds, such as those that eat small insects or swallow seeds whole, have a comparatively lighter, weaker structure here. From where the nasals and frontals join, the lacrimals extend sideways in front of — or anterior to — the eyes.

Behind the frontals lie the parietals, followed by the supraoccipital. All of these protect the brain on top. The foramen magnum is formed by the supraoccipital above, an exoccipital on either side, and the basioccipital below. The sides of the brain case are formed by the squamosals. Forward of each the postorbital bar projects down behind the orbit. Above and in front of the ear the squamosals bear a socket for the articulation of the quadrate bone, from which the lower jaw hinges. Underneath the skull and forward of the basioccipital, the basisphenoid houses the vital pituitary gland deep within it. Above and forward of the basisphenoid the parasphenoid, or basisphenoid rostrum, projects. On it the ethmoid rests, while from it the palatines extend forward to seat themselves between the premaxillaries and maxillaries, explained below. Between the palatines lies the slim sliver of the vomer, so easily lost in preparing a young chicken skull. Palatines and vomer help to form the roof of the mouth.

If you have followed this successfully you can see that we started at the tip of the beak, passed over the top of the skull, giving name and function of its parts, and arrived once more at the beak, but underneath it this time. Now we shall start backward again, beginning with the three bones that form the long slender rod of the "cheekbone." The maxilla, which bears teeth in us mammals but not in birds, extends backward from under the premaxilla and nasal bones. Posteriorly the maxilla partially overlaps the quadratojugal. Midway along this rod the jugal forms a splint that reinforces the overlap. Finally, the quadratojugal articulates with the quadrate, which forms the upper half of the jaw hinge. The "cheek-bone" forms a springy brace along the lower outer edge of the mouth between bill and quadrate for the support of the jaws, as well as providing an area of attachment for major jaw muscles.

Above the ear the quadrate articulates with the squamosal. Medially it is braced by the pterygoid, which extends from the quadrate to its sliding joint upon the parasphenoid. The anterior end of the pterygoid articulates with the posterior end of the palatine — and there you have it!

This complex and roundabout assembly of upper jawbones is relatively springy in many groups of birds. Flexibility acts as a shock absorber, especially in birds that, like the wood-peckers, give their bills a terrific beating.

Around the eyes are thin, overlapping, bony plates called the sclerotic ring. These protect and strengthen the eyeball. Fossil evidence shows that these were present in the ancestral backboned animals. The sclerotic ring has been lost in many groups and appears now only in certain fishes, reptiles, and birds.

The lower jaw is a relief in its simplicity. The slender light bones that form it give further evidence of the bird's reptilian ancestry. The triangular dentary forms the apex of the lower

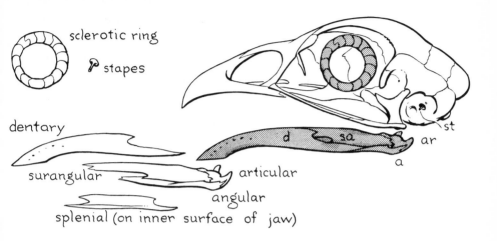

jaw. The surangular, splenial, angular, and articular form its backward-reaching arms. The articular, as its name states, articulates with the upper jaw at the base of the quadrate and forms the all-important jaw hinge. These several bones fuse in the adult and appear to be but one.

The tongue is supported by the hyoid apparatus. In the young bird this is extremely cartilaginous, and bony elements tend to take over as the bird matures. From the tongue, the hyoid extends posteriorly and divides into two arms lying

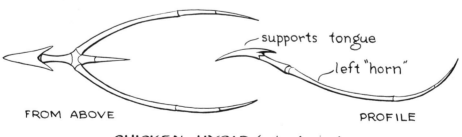

CHICKEN HYOID (actual size)

under the jaw. These "horns" slide forward to protrude the tongue. The flicker's tongue can be extended to a surprising length as it probes for insects. In order to provide for a hyoid long enough for this extension, the horns pass under the jaw, one on each side of the neck, up over the top of the brain case, and lead around together into the right nostril — leaving the left open for breathing. This extreme development of the hyoid in flickers is a beautiful example of the degree to which adaptation for a special way of life can alter a "normal" structure.

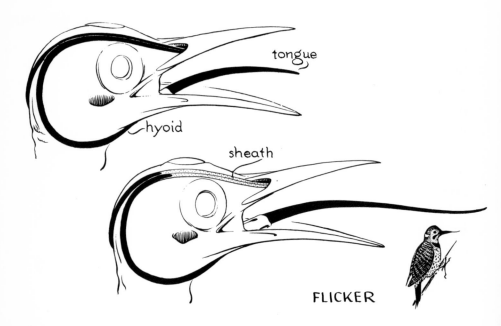

The very name vertebrate stresses the importance of the vertebrae in all animals with backbones. Its many bony elements give great flexibility and strength to the vertebral column. Numerous muscles arise from or insert into it. The ribs and pelvis articulate directly with it. From head to tail the spinal cord runs through it, protected by it. Nerves run in and out between the vertebrae to and from the spinal cord. Some major blood vessels follow it.

Unlike the situation in mammals the number of neck, or cervical, vertebrae varies in different groups of birds. The pigeon that will be used to describe the remainder of the skeleton has fourteen, while the mute swan has twenty-three. These cervical vertebrae bear short backward-pointed processes that are the remnants of ribs. On the last two cervical vertebrae, where the neck joins the body, the ribs become long but do not touch the sternum, a part described and shown on the next few pages. The shape of the vertebrae allows the neck to move in all directions. Birds can look almost directly backward and can reach almost every part of the body with the beak when preening. Aside from the neck and tail, there is little mobility in a bird's backbone, since great strength and rigidity are required for flight. A bird literally hangs from the central part of its backbone.

The thoracic vertebrae following the neck vertebrae bear complete ribs that do connect with the sternum. These vertebrae are rigid except between the hindmost where there is a somewhat movable joint. The last thoracic vertebra is completely fused with about twelve behind it to form the synsacrum, to which the

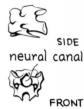

SIDE

neural canal

FRONT

CERVICAL VERTEBRA

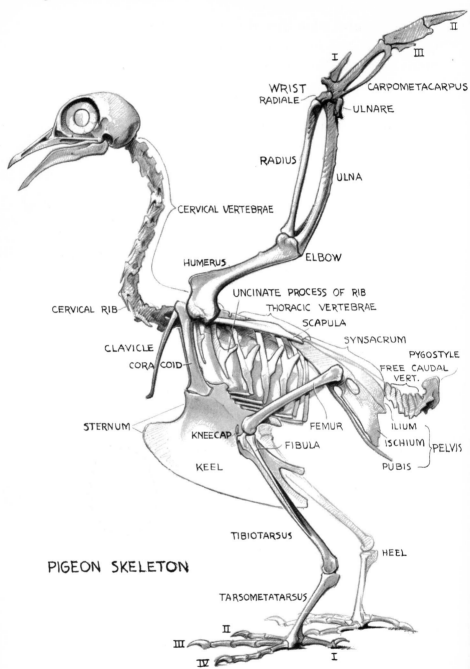

PIGEON SKELETON

hipbones, or pelvis, are also fused. The synsacrum, then, is a girder composed of one thoracic, about five lumbar, two sacral, and five caudal vertebrae.

Following the synsacrum are six movable tail, or caudal, vertebrae ending in the pygostyle, which is composed of about four or five of the remaining caudal vertebrae, completely fused. The pygostyle supports the tail feathers and the movable caudal vertebrae in front of it allow the flexibility necessary for this important part of the apparatus of flight.

The ribs are slender, flat bones. Each has two sections lying almost at right angles to one another. The upper or vertebral sections are articulated to the last two cervical and all the thoracic vertebrae. Small flat bones, the uncinates, project upward and backward from the ribs. Each of the uncinates overlaps the rib behind. This adds to the strength and stiffness of the entire rib cage to a degree out of all proportion to the size of these small bones. In the adult each uncinate is fused to its rib and looks like a simple projection. In the young they can be seen as separate bones. The lower, or sternal, portions of the five thoracic ribs are connected to the sternum. They are composed of bone in flying birds and of flexible cartilage in most flightless birds — and mammals. The ribs not only function as a protective cage for the vital parts they enclose but also act as compression members or struts between the sternum and the thoracic vertebrae.

The sternum is a thin plate of bone shaped like an elongated dish curving upward. From its lower midline projects the large keel that strengthens it and gives extra area and greater mechanical advantage for the attachment of the muscles powering flight.

The wings are supported by a tripod of strong bones collectively called the pectoral girdle. The heaviest of these, indeed

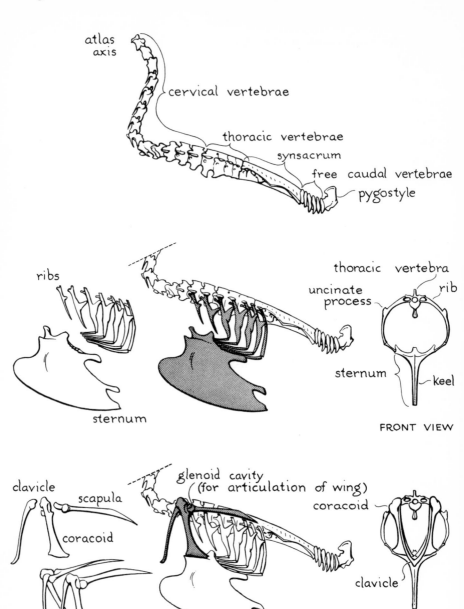

atlas
axis

cervical vertebrae

thoracic vertebrae

synsacrum

free caudal vertebrae

pygostyle

ribs

thoracic vertebra

uncinate
process

rib

sternum

sternum

keel

FRONT VIEW

clavicle

scapula

coracoid

glenoid cavity
(for articulation of wing)

coracoid

clavicle

pectoral girdle

FRONT VIEW

the heaviest bones in the bird's body, are the two
coracoids, the bases of which rest on the sternum.
In front of the coracoids hangs the furcula—
wishbone or merrythought, to use the delightful
older name. It consists of the right and left clavicles, the
collarbones in man, fused at the bottom by the interclavicle.
The upper ends of the clavicles, the part you hold when wish-
ing, articulate with the right and left coracoids. From this
point the shoulder blades, or scapulae, point directly backward over the ribs parallel to the backbone. Embedded in
muscle they firmly but flexibly anchor this part of the tripod
to the thorax. Where each scapula comes together with its
coracoid is the glenoid cavity, into which the head of the
upper wing bone (the humerus) fits. Thus the wings from
which the bird hangs while in flight are supported by the
pectoral girdle which rests, through the strong coracoids, on
the sternum. The sternum is connected to and held apart
from the rigid backbone by strong but flexible struts, the ribs.

Man has probably always fancied that if he could but make
wings he could strap them to his arms and, like Icarus, fly.
The unreality of this idea can be demonstrated by lying flat
on your face with arms spread and trying to lift your weight
even a few inches off the floor. Our puny chest muscles could
not support our heavy bodies in flight for an instant.

More than half the total muscular tissue and one fifth of
the weight of the entire bird may be concentrated in the

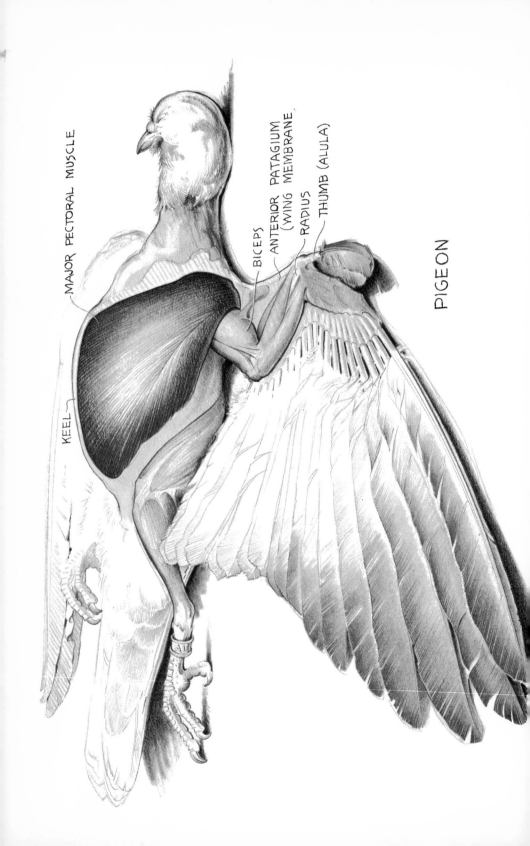

MAJOR PECTORAL MUSCLE

BICEPS

ANTERIOR PATAGIUM
(WING MEMBRANE)

RADIUS

THUMB (ALULA)

KEEL

PIGEON

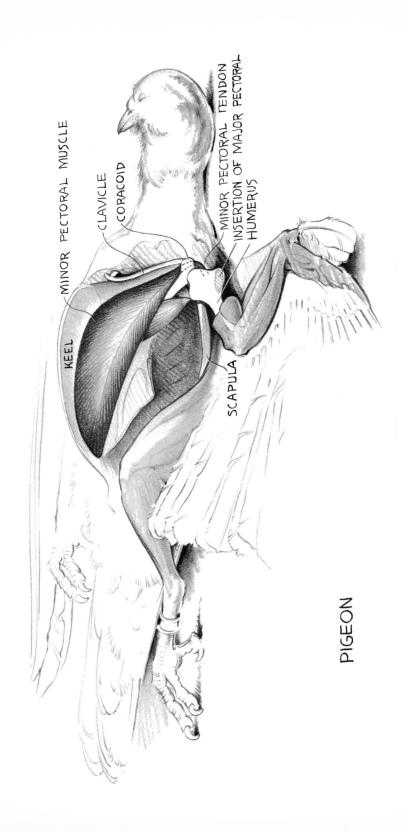

MINOR PECTORAL MUSCLE

CLAVICLE

CORACOID

MINOR PECTORAL TENDON

INSERTION OF MAJOR PECTORAL

HUMERUS

KEEL

SCAPULA

PIGEON

two great muscles of flight, the major and minor pectorals. These are the breast muscles, the familiar "white meat" of chickens and turkeys. In more powerful fliers the pectoral muscles are a dark rich red. This color is due to the great blood supply necessary to furnish these huge muscles with the energy needed to support the bird in the air under the tremendous stresses of flight. The major pectoral muscle arises from the entire lower part of the sternum's keel, the edges of the sternum, and the clavicle. Its fibers converge and attach, or insert, on the underside of a ridge that projects from the head of the humerus. The contraction of this mass of muscle pulls the wing powerfully downward with a force that could not be achieved without the added leverage obtained by its attachment to the keel. Bats, the only truly flying mammals, and pterodactyls, extinct flying reptiles, also developed keels for the same purpose. In birds such as ostriches, which have lost the power of flight, the keel has either become lost or is very small. But penguins, now flightless in air, actually do fly through the water and so have kept their keels.

The minor pectoral muscle, which raises the wing, also arises from the keel and sternum! It is much smaller than the major, lies under it, and has less power, because the up-

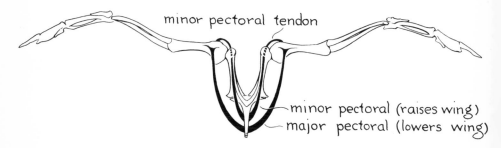

minor pectoral tendon

minor pectoral (raises wing)
major pectoral (lowers wing)

DIAGRAM OF MAJOR FLIGHT MUSCLES

stroke of the wing obviously takes but a fraction of the power needed for the downstroke.
Birds accomplish the seemingly impossible
task of raising the wing with a muscle located
beneath it by means of the long tendon of the
minor pectoral. This tendon passes up through
a hole formed at the juncture of the three bones
of the pectoral girdle—the clavicle, coracoid,
and scapula. This three-boned hole, the triosial
foramen, serves as an excellent pulley. The
tendon passes through it and inserts on the top
of the humerus. Thus, when the minor pectoral
contracts, the wing is raised. All other vertebrates that can pull their forelimbs dorsally use
muscles located on the back for this purpose.
Birds, in keeping with their need for a low center of gravity, cannot afford a muscle heavy
enough for this purpose high on the back and
have evolved this unique mechanism.

Many of the bones of the bird wing are iden-
tifiable as the same bones in the forelimb of a
land animal—modified for flight. The short,
strong humerus articulates with the pectoral
girdle at the glenoid cavity. There is a prominent ridge on the upper front surface of its head
for the insertion of the major pectoral muscle.
On the upper side of the head of the humerus
there is a smaller area, also marked by a ridge,
for insertion of the minor pectoral. The fore-
arm consists of the radius and ulna. This
strong combination of two bones is longer than
the humerus in most birds. The wrist of most

minor pectoral
insertion

RIDGE

major pectoral
insertion

LEFT HUMERUS

vertebrates consists of many small bones. But in birds only two of these bones remain as separate carpal bones, the radiale and the ulnare. The rest have become fused to the three fused metacarpals to become the carpometacarpus. Only three digits remain of the five of the primitive vertebrate hand, the thumb and the first two fingers — numbers one, two, and three (some anatomists maintain that the three bird digits represent numbers two, three, and four). The thumb moves freely and bears the three feathers of the alula, which is a small part of the wing of great importance in flight. Number two, the forefinger, is long and well developed. Its outermost segment, the terminal phalanx, is beautifully hollowed to receive the stout quill of the leading flight feather. Finger number three develops as a remnant with but one small phalanx.

The primary feathers originate on the hand, the secondaries from the posterior margin of the ulna, on which can be seen small rounded bumps of bone where the quills of these feathers articulate. Secondaries growing from the area of the elbow are often called tertiaries, especially in species where they vary noticeably from the rest of the secondaries. The scapular feathers grow from the shoulder.

All these flight feathers (the remiges) are partially covered by small shingled covert feathers and are supported by a long flat membrane. Frontward, there is another membrane, the anterior patagium, which stretches between the wrist and the shoulder. Covered with small covert feathers, this forms an important part of the flight surface of the wing. Posteriorly there is a smaller membrane, the posterior patagium, which stretches between the elbow and the body. Various muscles pull the bird's wing forward and back and rotate the humerus. Others extend or fold the wing. These are the same as our own triceps and biceps. They are easily

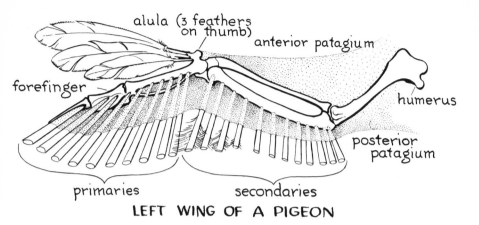

LEFT WING OF A PIGEON

seen, even without dissection, through the skin on the underside of an extended wing, along with other muscles that extend or bend the wrist. Movement of the flight feathers is
controlled by a complex system of tendons and small muscles
along the back of the hand. The alula may be moved separately by means of its own muscles.

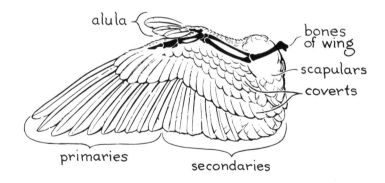

The pelvic girdle is elaborately shaped to meet the demands put upon it as the bird stands or moves. Like the ster-

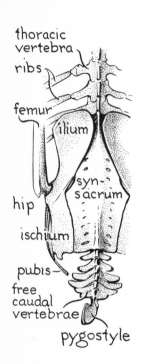

thoracic
vertebra
ribs
femur
ilium
syn-
sacrum
hip
ischium
pubis
free
caudal
vertebrae
pygostyle

SYNSACRUM AND PELVIS (from above)

num, its over-all shape is curved away from the direction of the main thrust exerted on it. Its large back, or dorsal, area affords room for the attachment of many muscles used chiefly in walking. Snug against its underside lie the kidneys. It supports and protects the sexual organs, intestines, and other vital parts contained within it.

Three almost paper-thin bones compose the pelvis on either side. The ilium abuts the synsacrum, the ischium fuses to the ilium below and to the rear, while the pubis forms a downward-, backward-pointing sliver parallel to the ischium. Where the ilium, ischium, and pubis meet a round hole is formed to make the hip socket for the head of the thighbone, or femur. The socket is called the acetabulum. The two halves of the pelvic girdle do not join underneath. This allows the heavy viscera to hang down, thus placing the center of gravity low.

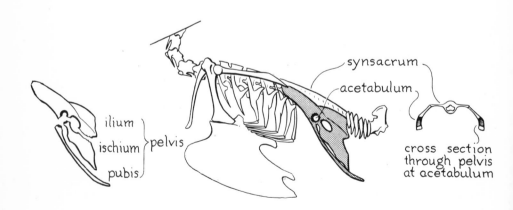

synsacrum
acetabulum
ilium
ischium $\Big\}$ pelvis
pubis
cross section
through pelvis
at acetabulum

The femur is quite short and can move forward and backward to some degree but not sideways as can the human femur when we spread our legs. Actually the bird femur is so short that it is often indistinguishable from the body upon casual examination of a live bird. The femur articulates with the tibia and fibula at the knee much as it does in man, complete with kneecap, or patella. More specifically, the tibia is the tibiotarsus, a fusion of the tibia, shinbone, and two of the tarsal, or ankle, bones. All that is left of the fibula in a bird's shin is the tiny sliver you doubtless have noticed while eating a drumstick. Next comes the tarsometatarsus, which, as its name implies, is a fusion of three more tarsals and three metatarsals. For comparison, the metatarsal bones in man form the arch of the foot. The digits of the bird foot are reduced from the primitive five. The usual number is four, with the "big toe," number one, pointed backward as a brace and for clasping a perch. Two, three, and four point forward in most birds. It can now be seen that a bird stands on its toes with the heel off the ground like a cat or a dog. This is the digitigrade position, in contrast to standing with the heel on the ground (plantigrade position) as man does. However, man goes up on his toes in the manner of the bird, cat, or dog for speed when running.

Although a bird stands on two legs like a man, it does not do this in the same way. To

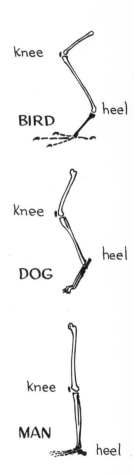

simulate the bird's posture bend your body forward until it is almost parallel to the ground, bend your knees until they almost touch the chest, and stand on your toes. In about one second you will find that this is a very uncomfortable as well as ludicrous position for a human. The bird overcomes this difficulty by means of the long pelvis and synsacrum in combination with the forward directed femur, imbedded in muscle, which throws the main point of support forward, distributing weight in a more balanced and comfortable way.

The leg of the great blue heron, illustrated opposite, is almost a caricature of attenuation, and serves well to show in the extreme an adaptation for flight found in all birds — the tendency for the heavy fleshy "business" ends of the muscles to be concentrated as near the body as possible. Weight is thus kept near the center of gravity, while only long light tendons extend to the extremities.

An interesting feature of the leg muscles of many species is the presence of a device that locks a bird to its perch. As the leg bends, tendons running to the toes can automatically tighten and cause the toes to grasp. In this way the crouched bird is clamped to its perch and can relax without fear of falling.

This automatic flexion of toes also works with some birds of prey. The great horned owl has a fearful set of talons on its four toes. When the owl strikes its prey the toes grasp automat-

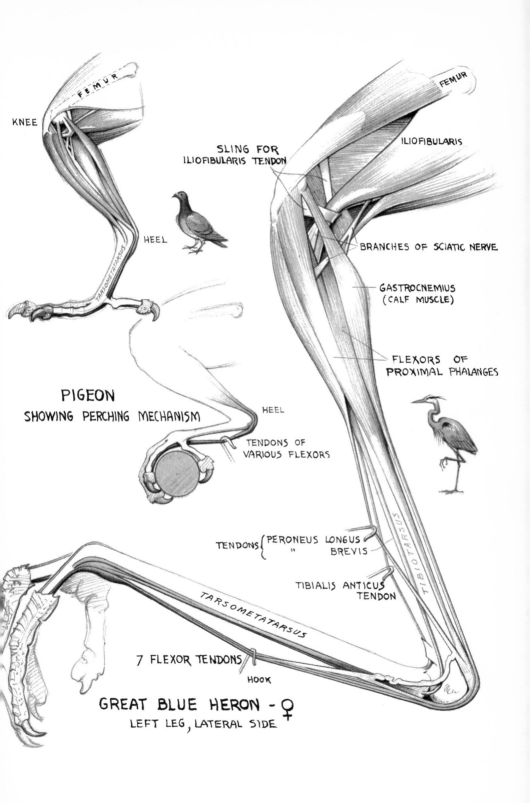

FEMUR

KNEE

HEEL

TARSOMETATARSUS

SLING FOR
ILIOFIBULARIS TENDON

FEMUR

ILIOFIBULARIS

BRANCHES OF SCIATIC NERVE

GASTROCNEMIUS
(CALF MUSCLE)

FLEXORS OF
PROXIMAL PHALANGES

PIGEON
SHOWING PERCHING MECHANISM

HEEL

TENDONS OF
VARIOUS FLEXORS

TENDONS { PERONEUS LONGUS
"   BREVIS

TIBIALIS ANTICUS
TENDON

TIBIOTARSUS

TARSOMETATARSUS

7 FLEXOR TENDONS

HOOK

GREAT BLUE HERON - ♀
LEFT LEG, LATERAL SIDE

LEFT LEG OF GREAT HORNED OWL

ically as the weight of the body bends the legs. Once imbedded, the sharp curved talons work like double ice tongs
and the struggles or weight of the prey only serve to sink
them deeper.

Like the bird's beak, its feet run through a whole gamut of
variety of shapes and functions, enabling it to live in different
environments. Woodpeckers have two of the four bird toes

pointing backward, and, with the help of very stiff tail feathers, they serve to give the bird the extra bracing it needs as it climbs vertical tree trunks. Adaptations for swimming are clearly visible in ducks, gulls, loons, cormorants, and other web-footed birds.

The grebe's swimming apparatus is quite different. In place of webbed toes only, the entire foot, including the tarsometatarsus as well as the paddlelike toes, becomes the means of propulsion. This beautiful example of special adaptation is seen in the formation of the scales of the foot and in the delicate skeleton within. The tarsometatarsal bone is somewhat flattened and the bones of each toe become progressively flattened until they are capped by the flat nail that has itself become incorporated into the paddle. The long tibiotarsus articulates with the short femur in a most unusual joint that allows the entire lower leg to rotate outward to an extreme degree. Because of this the grebe's small flat feet are able to perform as a most efficient propelling device.

Even the color of the feet follows this peculiar adaptation.

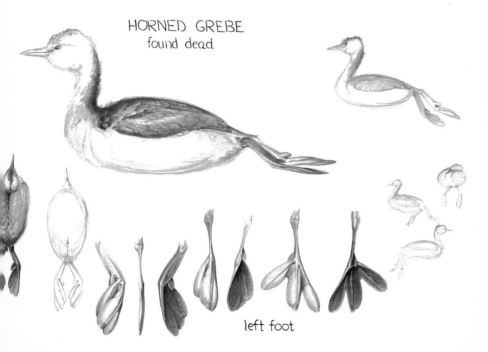

HORNED GREBE
found dead

left foot

A grebe's feet are light on the *inner* surface and dark on the *outer*. As the leg is rotated in swimming, the outside surface becomes uppermost. This surface matches the grebe's dark back, and the inside, now undermost, matches the light gray underbody. The protective countershading of dark above and light below is thus flawlessly preserved.

Such is the beauty and marvel found in a few details of an organism that is only one of the countless products of 2000 million years of changing, adapting life. Discovering for ourselves these intricate technical details made an exciting adventure out of the finding of a dead grebe on the beach one winter's afternoon.

The muscles we have mentioned are a small but prominent fraction of the total. Others move the tongue, tail, eyelids, jaws, and so on — all under conscious control. These are the striated muscles. Innumerable muscles of a different type are not under conscious control. Thousands are located just beneath the skin for the purpose of ruffling, smoothing, or otherwise moving the contour feathers. These smooth muscles are also found in the digestive tract, circulatory vessels, genital organs, and elsewhere. Still another type of muscle is found in the heart alone.

Here you have every reason to wonder, "How is it known that what appears to be one bone is actually made up of many fused bones? How is it known that certain bones have been lost and were not always absent? There are several ways in which these facts are determined. In the developing embryo or in the very young much of the skeleton can be seen to be composed of many separate bones that subsequently appear as one in the adult. While these may be fused in the adults of some groups they may remain separate, or partially so, in others.

Also, the science of paleontology, through the study of fossils, gives many clues. In *Archaeopteryx*, the oldest fossil bird now known, only a few of the vertebrae in the sacral region and none in the long tail were fused. In modern birds many vertebrae have become fused to form the synsacrum, while the tail consists of but a few movable vertebrae followed by those fused into the pygostyle. None of these are fused completely in the embryo bird. It becomes clear that the vertebrae in the sacral area and tail of birds have become more fused as they evolved. The three bones forming the tarsometatarsus in the embryo pigeon are almost indistinguishably fused in the adult. In the penguin they remain distinct through life.

We have been talking about the ways of knowing how one part can be made up of many fused parts. The *loss* of parts is known in similar ways. The reptiles from which *Archaeopteryx* descended, *Archaeopteryx*, and later extinct birds had teeth. It is plain to see that as birds evolved they lost their teeth. *Archaeopteryx* had three distinct reptile-like clawed fingers — modern bird's fingers are much reduced in size and parts and almost none have claws. Many of the vertebrae in *Archaeopteryx*'s long tail have vanished completely in modern birds. Comparative studies of both extinct and recent animals give countless other examples of fusion as well as loss.

Many bones and other anatomical features

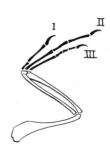

ARCHAEOPTERYX

PIGEON

are common to all vertebrates. They can be identified in different animals through a study of development and their relationships to each other although their shape, and often function, has changed a good deal. For instance, the humerus of an amphibian, a reptile, a bird, and a mammal is easily seen to be the same bone common to these widely separate animals and inherited from their common lobe-finned fish ancestor. Any part that is related in origin, no matter how modified for various functions it has become, is said to be homologous.

On the other hand any part that is different in origin but has a common function is said to be analogous. A bird's and an insect's wings are analogous.

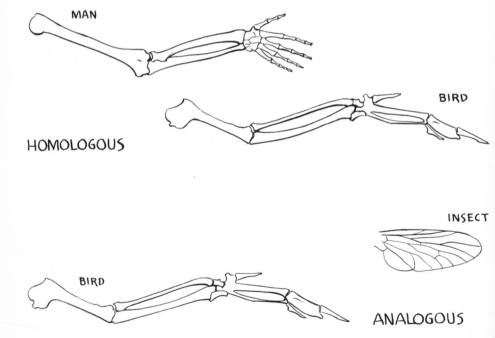

MAN

BIRD

HOMOLOGOUS

INSECT

BIRD

ANALOGOUS

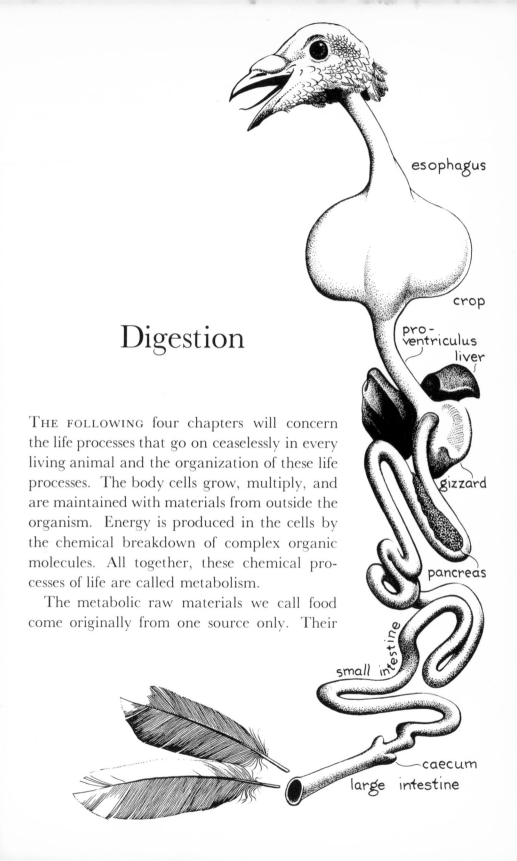

Digestion

THE FOLLOWING four chapters will concern the life processes that go on ceaselessly in every living animal and the organization of these life processes. The body cells grow, multiply, and are maintained with materials from outside the organism. Energy is produced in the cells by the chemical breakdown of complex organic molecules. All together, these chemical processes of life are called metabolism.

The metabolic raw materials we call food come originally from one source only. Their

esophagus

crop

pro-
ventriculus

liver

gizzard

pancreas

small intestine

caecum

large intestine

matter is composed from minerals of the earth and carbon dioxide and oxygen from the air. The potential energy contained in their complex chemical structure comes from the sun. Plants can manufacture their own food directly from nonliving matter by use of the sun's energy during the process of photosynthesis. Animals cannot, and must subsist upon plant food or upon animals that have eaten plants. Consequently, plants are the primary source of all food — the basis of all life. So birds and men, fleas and whales all have the same beginning in the energy of the sun and the fertility of the earth and atmosphere.

Oxygen and food (carbohydrates, fats, and proteins) are distributed about the body by the blood. The wastes of metabolism, carbon dioxide, surplus water, and nitrogenous end products (mostly uric acid in birds) are picked up by the blood and carried to various organs for removal. Much of the plant and animal food eaten by animals must be broken down into simpler chemical compounds before it can be transported by the blood and absorbed by the cells. The proteins especially must be broken down into their simpler components, the amino acids. This is the function of the digestive system.

The digestive system is fundamentally a tube running through an animal from its mouth to its anus. Along the tube are glands that secrete chemicals to break the food down into substances the cells of the body can assimilate. In simple animals like sea urchins, the digestive system is just this and no more; but in higher forms of life, like birds, it has become a complex assembly line for treating foods both chemically and physically, so that energy in them can be better assimilated by the body.

In the bird mouth are salivary glands that secrete moist

saliva for lubrication of the food. Some birds, particularly
water feeders, are almost without them. This saliva contains
no digestive enzymes. The roof of the bird's mouth is hard
and horny. It is divided along the midline by a deep fissure
separating the hard palate into two long folds. The depression between these is lined with backward-pointing horny
papillae. The tongue is small and also bears backward-
pointing papillae that assist in manipulating food and swallowing, and doubtless prevents the sometimes still-squirming
prey from escaping.

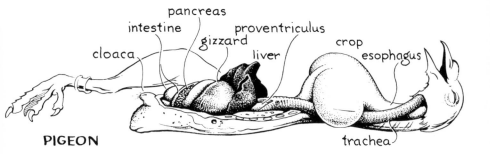

PIGEON

The gullet, or esophagus, is a thin-walled flabby tube ex-
tending downward to the base of the neck, where it expands
into the balloon-like crop. Birds can swallow with nonchalant ease large hard objects that would choke a man. The
size of the crop varies from almost nothing in some meat
eaters to a huge sac in grain eaters like the pigeon. Food is
stored and moistened in it and passed on to the stomach.
The lining of a pigeon's crop becomes specialized during the
breeding season and forms "pigeon's milk" a custardy substance that is sloughed off and regurgitated to the young. Its
chemical makeup is amazingly similar to the milk of mammals.

In zoology courses the animals used for dissection are usually kept in Formalin or some other preservative. The crop in these specimens appears as a thickened bag of leathery skin and the rest of the organs are equally unattractive. This gives the student a sorry idea of the beauty of the interior of an animal. Before dissecting a fresh poultry-store pigeon to make the drawings here, we filled the crop with air and tied off the gullet. The dissection had to be done with the utmost caution so that the inflated crop would not be punctured. The result was rewarding. The crop lay exposed as clear as a soap bubble and almost as delicate. A few kernels of corn still lay in it, clearly visible. We phoned a friend, a gentle woman who is deeply squeamish, she thought, about "innards." Her curiosity conquered her squeamishness and she came, looked, marveled, and went back to the birds at her feeding station with a new dimension of appreciation.

The bird's stomach has two parts. The forward section, the proventriculus, is a soft organ where food is treated with digestive enzymes secreted by its glands. The posterior section is the gizzard, or ventriculus. It is lined with heavy, ridged, cornified epithelium and has strong muscular walls. The grinding action of these powerful muscles is combined with the abrasion of small stones, which many birds swallow, and creates a living mill capable of crushing the hardest food. Here are the "teeth"

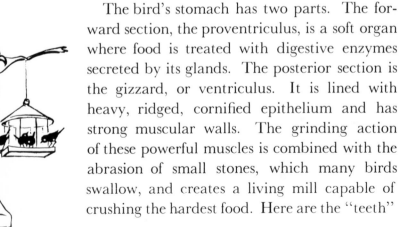

of a bird. In many carnivorous birds with their soft high-protein diet, the gizzard has more the character of a usual stomach.

Most digestion takes place in the small intestine, where innumerable microscopic glands secrete digestive enzymes. The small intestine is long in birds. Their high metabolic rate, in keeping with their active life, requires a large digestive and absorptive surface for the great quantities of food taken in. The large, lobed liver and the pancreas send bile and pancreatic juices through ducts into the upper end of the small intestine. Depending upon species, a gall bladder may or may not be present. As the food moves along, the digested part is absorbed through the walls of the intestine. At the juncture of the small intestine and the rectum are the two saclike caeca. Food enters these but their function is not entirely known. Grain-eating birds generally have larger caeca than others, and this increases the absorptive area of their digestive systems. In some grass or grain-eating species the cellulose of the vegetable fiber is broken down and made available by bacterial action in the caeca. Rabbits have a huge caecum and man an atrophied bothersome one, his appendix. However, it has not been established that the caeca of bird and mammal are homologous.

From the intestine undigested or indigestible waste material moves to the rectum. There any excess water is extracted for retention by the body, and the feces are partly solidified.

The digestive, urinary, and reproductive organs all have their exits in the cloaca (Latin for sewer). Only in mammals do these exits have separate openings on the exterior of the body. In the cloaca some water is reabsorbed from the urine. The urine mixes with the feces and is seen as the white in bird droppings.

The metabolism of birds is so high that energy is speedily

used up. Carnivorous birds digest large quantities of food very rapidly. The seed eaters have longer intestines than meat eaters and take longer to assimilate the greater quantities of less nourishing food; but berry eaters like our pet cedar waxwing may eject in fifteen minutes the pit of fruit they have swallowed. All birds seem to be constantly swallowing at one end and ejecting at the other. Some species even use this ready ammunition in dive-bombing tactics against marauders in their nesting grounds.

Terrific food requirements may cause birds to starve to death quickly when food is unobtainable, especially in cool weather. Small birds are especially vulnerable, since in addition to an extra-high metabolic rate the ratio of their outside heat-losing surface is proportionally larger to their volume than that of bigger birds. When a bird is found apparently whole but listless and sick, it is often starved and has used up its reserves of energy past the point of being saved.

Chemical reactions double with each ten-degree rise in temperature. Birds have the highest body heat of any animals, between 104 and 112 degrees Fahrenheit, or higher, making man's 98.6 seem cool by comparison. Therefore the chemical reactions in a bird's body are, on an average, double those in our own.

Stray nestlings inevitably turn up in the homes of those interested in birds. Keeping these waifs alive is a desperate job. It can be done successfully only by duplicating closely the activities of the parent birds. This means plenty of proper food for the gaping youngster every half hour or so. After a bout with this frantic occupation one's respect for parent birds goes up. Constant warmth is also necessary. Hot-water bottles are good for emergencies, but we have found an ordinary heating pad with temperature control to be a handy household item during the spring and early summer. Actually it is best to give these young birds a merciful death, unless you are willing and able to devote hours a day to their care.

Circulation

THE CIRCULATORY SYSTEM of backboned animals consists of a network of blood vessels running to every part of the animal. The smallest of these, the hair-fine capillaries, carry the life-giving food and oxygen which blood contains to every cell in the body, where they are exchanged for the wastes of the life processes. This system is closed, with no beginning and no end. Along it are way stations that supply the sustenance, renew the cells that carry some of it, and remove waste that has been picked up. The system is operated by the heart, a muscled pump that forces the blood throughout the vast and endless network. The circulatory system also plays a vital part in the battle against disease, the maintenance of temperature in birds and mammals, the repair of injury, and the distribution of the hormones. With a low-power microscope it is a simple and awe-inspiring experience to look through the skin of a small living animal and watch the red blood cells smoothly flowing along the vessels. We used a young newt to demonstrate the circulatory system to a couple of young humans. The newt lay still, unknowingly aiding two small boys to see what went on in an amphibian capillary and so to understand themselves the better.

Closely associated with the circulatory system is the lymphatic system. Its thin-walled vessels parallel the venous system in many ways, and collect plasma-like fluid that fills spaces in body cavities and among cells. Eventually lymph moves into larger and larger vessels, until it empties into veins in the upper part of the body and so enters the circulatory system. In most vertebrates lymph is moved through lymph vessels only by pressure from bodily movement in nearby tissues, but pulsing lymph hearts are present in the embryos of many birds and, although these atrophy in many after hatching, they remain functional in the perching birds, ducks, and a few others.

The lymphatic system transports some fats, picks up waste materials from the tissues, and aids in fighting infection by means of white blood cells. In many vertebrates the lymph nodes filter out impurities, and bacteria are destroyed in them. Lymph nodes have been found in few birds.

Birds and mammals are the only animals in whose circulatory systems the venous blood — that returning from the body capillaries carrying carbon dioxide — is completely separated in the heart from arterial blood — that which has been replenished with oxygen in the lungs. The heart in these two classes is really a double pump. The right side handles only venous blood, while the left side simultaneously pumps only oxygenated arterial blood. The blood returning from the body capillaries with its load

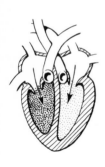

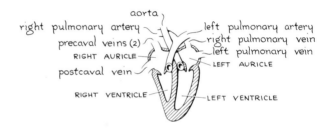

DIAGRAM OF A BIRD HEART

of carbon dioxide reaches the right auricle through two pre- and one postcaval (superior and inferior caval) veins. It passes into the right ventricle and is pumped through the pulmonary artery, which sends a branch to each lung. When the carbon dioxide has been exchanged for oxygen as the blood flows through the lung capillaries, it returns to the left auricle along the pulmonary veins. It then enters the left ventricle and is pumped, in birds, through

the single right aortic arch into the innominate arteries, the dorsal aorta, and their branches. By these paths it flows throughout the entire body, picking up its load of food, exchanging it and oxygen for wastes, and flowing back into the right auricle and ventricle of the heart once more to continue its endless circulation.

The separate but continuous flow of venous and arterial blood, combined with a system of valves that control the rate of circulation, make high blood pressure and a more rapid distribution of the materials of life possible. Only birds and mammals attain the metabolic rates that result from this system. Birds average a higher rate than mammals. But both are unique among all living things in their ability to maintain and regulate their body temperature independently of

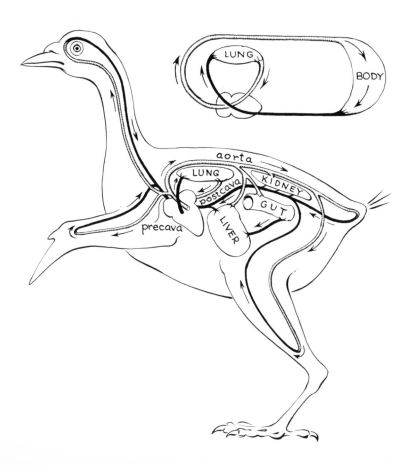

that of the environment — within limits, of course. The "warm-blooded" birds and mammals are called homeothermic (same heat) animals. Fishes, amphibians, and reptiles, the so called "cold-blooded" animals, are dull, sluggish creatures by comparison.

The size and rate of heartbeat are proportionally large in the fast-living birds when compared to those of most mammals. However, these vary with the size and activity of the species. In general the smaller, more active birds have proportionally larger hearts, faster pulses, and higher temperatures than larger, less active birds. The heart of the mute swan is about 8 per cent of its weight, that of the starling 11 and the hummingbird 20 per cent. The pigeon's heart beats 192 times a minute and the sparrow's over 500. The swan has a temperature of 105 degrees Fahrenheit and the swift 111 degrees. The smallest bird, the bee hummingbird, probably has the fastest metabolic rate of any living vertebrate. It has been calculated to be fifty times that of man when the bird is at rest.

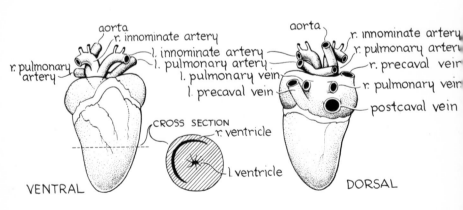

PIGEON HEART (actual size)

Breathing

BIRDS, so vibrantly active inside and out, use huge quantities of oxygen. Consequently the avian respiratory system is the most extraordinary of any in the vertebrate world. It consists of a pair of smallish lungs plus a complex of delicate air sacs located in various parts of the body. The air sacs act as momentary storehouses for large amounts of air and thus are accessories to the lungs, to lighten the bird in proportion to its over-all size and, perhaps, as an internal cooling system. But the entire function of the respiratory system is not as yet well understood.

The bird's nostrils open into the roof of the mouth through two internal nares. Just behind the base of the tongue is the slitlike glottis, the opening into the windpipe. A bird's glottis closes simply by squeezing together and does not have the flap valve, or epiglottis, found in mammals. To see the glottis in action look into the wide-open mouth of a hungry young nestling. William Beebe wrote, with great scientific detachment as far as the infant bird in the experiment was concerned: "No matter how suddenly you may eject a stream of water into a bird's mouth, reflex action will anticipate the danger of choking and close the aperture." Man apparently does not react so quickly, for we frequently get things down our "Sunday throats."

The glottis opens into the larynx. In mammals, frogs, toads, and a few reptiles the vocal cords located here produce what sounds they make. To us, one of the world's most satisfying sounds and the surest sign that spring has really come is the song of that minute treefrog, the spring peeper. At first, on some still March night, there are but one or two timorous trills. As the weather warms, more and more peepers join the chorus, until the night — so quiet all winter — fairly vibrates with this first song of stirring life. To the world, filled with human trouble, spring comes once more as it always has, and the peeper sings as it has sung for about 40,000,000 years. It is a soothing expe-

rience to go out into the warm spring evening and, by patient stalking, pick out a singing peeper in the rays of a flashlight. If you are motionless for a moment you can stoop beside him. There he sits, a tiny being on a blade of grass, calling for his mate as though the resonating bubble at his throat would burst.

We started to say that birds have a larynx. Similar to those of the other vertebrates, it is a chamber leading into the windpipe from the glottis. However, there are no vocal cords in birds' larynges and no sound is produced in them. You can understand how we got into peeper instead of bird song at this point. The larynx leads into the windpipe, or trachea. This tube is stiffened by rings, which in many birds, including the pigeon, are of bone ventrally and cartilage dorsally. The rings allow the tube to bend freely but keep it from pinching or collapsing, so the vital air supply is always open. This seems simple enough until one remembers that this tube must remain unkinked even when the supple bird neck is turned, twisted, drawn in, or stretched out in the many positions of preening or feeding. To make this possible the membrane between the rings is extremely elastic, and the rings themselves are often remarkably formed. They vary a good deal, both in shape and degree of boniness, in different groups of birds.

The trachea leads down parallel and ventral to the soft esophagus, except where the crop bulges over it in some birds, and passes between the arms of the wishbone. Here it splits into two smaller tubes, the bronchi, each leading to a lung. The construction of the bronchi resembles a trachea that has been split lengthwise. The outer walls have half-rings but the inner walls are flat and composed of membrane alone.

Where the trachea forks into the bronchi is, at last, the

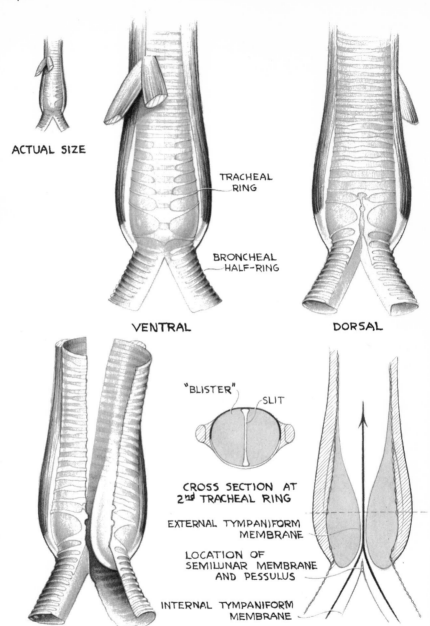

ACTUAL SIZE

TRACHEAL
RING

BRONCHEAL
HALF-RING

VENTRAL

DORSAL

"BLISTER"   SLIT

CROSS SECTION AT
2nd TRACHEAL RING

EXTERNAL TYMPANIFORM
MEMBRANE

LOCATION OF
SEMILUNAR MEMBRANE
AND PESSULUS

INTERNAL TYMPANIFORM
MEMBRANE

SYRINX OF A PIGEON

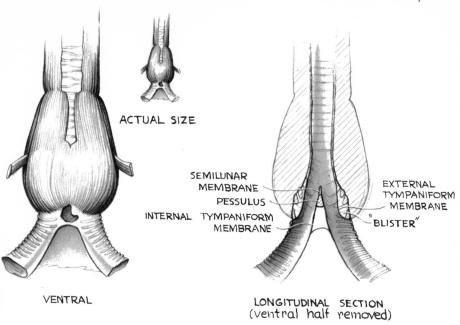

ACTUAL SIZE

SEMILUNAR
MEMBRANE
PESSULUS
INTERNAL TYMPANIFORM
MEMBRANE

EXTERNAL
TYMPANIFORM
MEMBRANE

"BLISTER"

VENTRAL

LONGITUDINAL SECTION
(ventral half removed)

SYRINX OF A STARLING

vocal organ of birds, the syrinx — found in no other animals.
Among various groups of birds the syrinx varies greatly in
shape, complexity, and even in position. For our description
we shall keep to the syrinx in pigeons. In these birds the
lower tracheal rings are modified to support a slightly expanded chamber. Where the internal tympaniform membranes, which form the inner walls of the bronchi, come
together they form a seam like that between the legs of a pair
of pants. The pessulus, a bony or cartilaginous sliver, is present here in most birds. It helps to support the internal tympaniform membranes as well as the semilunar membrane, an
extension of the tympaniform membranes which protrudes
into the syrinx. In the pigeons we dissected, we found the
pessulus small or absent, and the semilunar membrane in a

similar state; in other groups these can be well-developed.

On the inside lateral walls of the pigeon syrinx are two mucus-filled "blisters" which form a slit between them. These are the external tympaniform membranes. In specimens that have been preserved in alcohol or Formalin these tend to shrink so that their size and importance is overlooked. Under the same conditions the pessulus ridge between the bronchi hardens and its appearance is exaggerated. We believe that many an anatomist has been misled by not working with absolutely fresh material. Textbook errors abound and are perpetuated by writers who use them for reference without re-examination of the real thing.

Muscles along the outer walls of the trachea control the shape of the syrinx and its membranes. When air is exhaled, vibrations of the membranes create the pigeon's soft-voiced *coo*. In other species other syringes make sounds ranging from the sweetest melody to the most rasping squawks. The shape of the larynx and other modifications of the trachea amplify and modify sounds originating in the syrinx. The finest singers do not necessarily have the fanciest syringes. Some songbirds have much simpler ones than do those birds that only squawk or quack. The mallard drake has a complicated asymmetric syrinx-drum. His voice is but a soft *wheep wheep*. Although the hen mallard has no bulge in the syrinx it is she

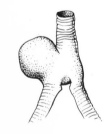

SYRINX OF A
MALLARD DRAKE

that does the well-known loud quacking. The whooping
crane's trachea is four feet long, a coiled bugle, half of which
is contained within the keel of the sternum. The strange
thing is that many birds with regular trumpets for voices
make out well with the simple standard arrangement.

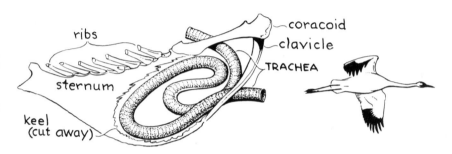

SECTION OF TRACHEA WITHIN KEEL OF WHOOPING CRANE

"This is all very well," you may say, "but it does not truly
explain that 'first fine careless rapture' of the bird song I
heard this morning." No, of course not; but it does in part
reveal the mechanism that made the song — a subtle mechanism whose function would be as lovely to the eye of any
poet, should he but see it, as the sound of the song to his ear.

Bird lungs are small, pink, foamy organs flattened against
the ribs on either side of the backbone. From them the air
sacs spread out through every major part of the body. These
are bladders with almost the texture of soap bubbles. They
are incredibly complex in shape, squeezing into available
spaces between and around other organs, and are completely
unlike the simple diagrams ordinarily seen. As with the other
anatomical drawings in this book, we set out to make a com-

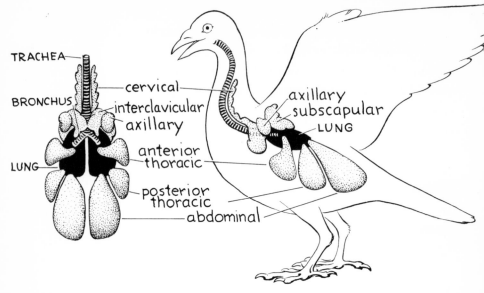

TRACHEA

BRONCHUS

LUNG

cervical

interclavicular
axillary

anterior
thoracic

posterior
thoracic

abdominal

axillary
subscapular

LUNG

DIAGRAM OF AIR SACS

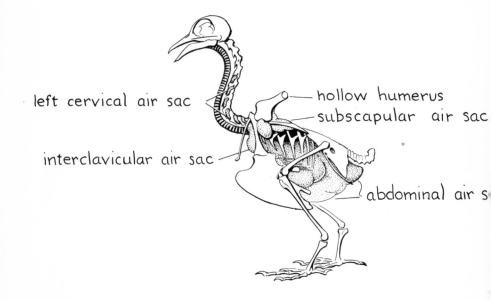

left cervical air sac

interclavicular air sac

hollow humerus

subscapular air sac

abdominal air s

RESPIRATORY SYSTEM OF A PIGEON

plex matter as clear as possible with the aid of drawings from our own dissections. The difficulty of doing this with the air sacs was insurmountable without unlimited time and facilities. We cannot show something so unbelievably delicate and complex in its three dimensions on a two-dimensional surface.

However, a description plus some diagrammatic drawing makes the principle simple enough. A pair of abdominal sacs extend into the viscera, a pair of posterior thoracic sacs, preceded by a pair of anterior thoracic sacs, lie forward of these. Beneath the clavicles lies the interclavicular air sac, paired in the embryo but usually fused into one in the adult. One of its several branches lies under each scapular, to become subscapular air sacs, while still another lies under each wingpit to become axillary air sacs. Along the neck lie the long cervical air sacs.

In other vertebrates air simply passes through the bronchi into each lung and out again every time it is inhaled and exhaled. This condition is relatively simple — and relatively inefficient. Man, for instance, uses only a small part of the oxygen in the air he breathes. Also, there is always a residue of dead air left in the lungs. This situation is good enough for a mammal but would be completely inadequate for birds. In them, except for a branch leading outward to a posterior thoracic air sac, each bronchus passes directly through its lung on the way to

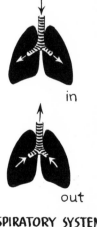

in

out

RESPIRATORY SYSTEM
OF A MAMMAL

its abdominal air sac. From the main channel of each bronchus in the lung smaller tubules branch out in orderly sequence dorsally and ventrally, while from these still smaller tubules the parabronchi—tiny air capillaries—connect everything with everything else.

Forward, immediately upon entering the ventral side of the lung, each bronchus forms three branches, one leading to the cervical, one to the interclavicular, and one to the anterior thoracic air sac. From some of these, additional air spaces extend into the humerus and other hollow bones of many birds.

Throughout the lung the pulmonary artery and the pulmonary vein branch to form anastomosing blood capillaries. When air is inhaled a fraction is diverted to the lungs through the air tubules. Between these air tubules and the blood capillaries an exchange of carbon dioxide for oxygen is constantly being made. The blood is then returned with its load of fresh oxygen to the heart via the pulmonary veins.

Nevertheless, most of the air inhaled by a bird passes unused through the lungs directly into the air sacs. When it is exhaled, that momentarily stored in the sacs is passed back through the air capillaries of the lungs, where it is then used. In a sense, a bird takes two breaths for every one it inhales, since fresh air passes through the lungs both coming and going. There is no dead space or unused air as in other vertebrates. In some diving birds the air may be passed back and forth between the lungs and air sacs several times while the bird is submerged, until every bit of oxygen has been absorbed.

How incredibly ingenious seems this solution to the problem of bird breathing! The forces of changing life, directed by adaptation, have hit upon a mechanism that solves two problems at once. Not only do birds have small lungs in keeping with the scheme of over-all lightness demanded in a flying animal, but they are able to breathe with greater efficiency than do animals with proportionately larger, heavier lungs.

The air sacs may also serve to cool the hot fires of bird metabolism. Many mammals get rid of excess heat by means of the blood capillaries of the skin. These contract and expand, depending upon the outside temperature, and radiate heat at varying rates. In warm weather, radiation is helped a good deal by the cooling effect of evaporating sweat. But birds have no cooling sweat glands in their skin, and feathers are such good insulators that this method of losing heat would be ineffective. The only other surfaces constantly exposed to cool air are the mouth, lungs, and air sacs. Birds pant in hot weather as do dogs, whose sweat glands are greatly reduced in number.

The thorax of a bird is so rigid that very little expansion and contraction is possible. While the bird is at rest the air is drawn into the lungs by a complex muscular action that slightly enlarges the thorax as well as the abdominal cavity, the location of the thoracic and abdominal air sacs. This causes inhalation while the contraction of the same cavities exhales air. In flapping flight similar action takes place automatically. Ventilation of the lungs is assumed to be synchronized with the up- and downstrokes of the wings. Each downstroke of the wing probably compresses the sternum and causes exhalation, which in birds is the more important and effective of the two movements of breathing.

The respiratory system of birds is also more efficient than that of mammals because of the rapid *rate* of breathing. Man breathes about 16 times a minute, the pigeon 25 or 30 times, and the hummingbird 250 times a minute while at rest. In flight the pigeon may take as many as 450 breaths a minute. It is hard to imagine how rapidly a hummingbird must breathe during flight. If the breathing of this bird is correlated with the frequency of its wingstroke, the number would be above 2000 a minute!

The Urogenital System

IT MAY SEEM strange to talk of the urinary and reproductive systems together, since they have absolutely separate functions. But their relation in the body is so close anatomically that it is difficult to speak of one without referring to the other.

The kidneys aid in keeping the internal environment at a fairly constant level. One function is to extract certain wastes and impurities from the blood. Some of these are substances that have been brought in with the food and cannot be used by the body cells. Other impurities, the most important, are the by-products of protein metabolism, the nitrogenous wastes. The greatest part of these is ammonia, which is poisonous but has been changed into harmless uric acid by the liver previous to its extraction from the blood and excretion by the kidney.

Another job of the kidneys is the maintenance of the correct

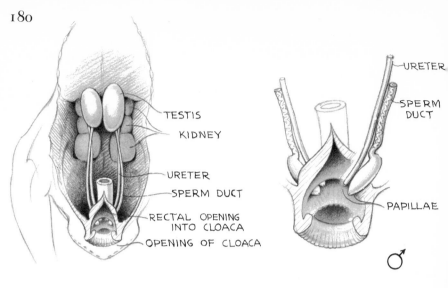

TESTIS

KIDNEY

URETER

SPERM DUCT

RECTAL OPENING
INTO CLOACA

OPENING OF CLOACA

URETER

SPERM
DUCT

PAPILLAE

♂

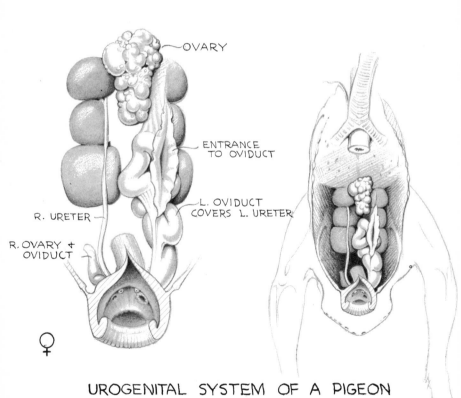

OVARY

ENTRANCE
TO OVIDUCT

L. OVIDUCT
COVERS L. URETER

R. URETER

R. OVARY &
OVIDUCT

♀

UROGENITAL SYSTEM OF A PIGEON

amounts of various salts in the fluids of the body, an adjustment necessary to maintain a healthy environment for the living cells. The amount of salt intake is up to the digestive system. But if this is too great the kidneys remove the excess, within limits. They also, when necessary, remove or conserve water and maintain its balance in the body fluids.

The kidneys of a pigeon are dark brown three-lobed organs that lie just posterior to the lungs in a depression of the dorsal wall formed by the synsacrum. The ureter, a threadlike duct, extends backward from each kidney to the cloaca. Birds have no bladders. The weight of such a storage chamber and particularly its contents would be a decided handicap in flight. So the urine moves directly to the cloaca, where it mixes partially with the solid feces and is voided almost at once.

In male birds the two whitish testes lie within the body anterior and ventral to the kidneys. From each a minute microscopically convoluted duct, the *vas deferens*, leads back to the cloaca, where its exit is marked by a papilla. No male birds except ducks, ostriches, and a few others have a penis.

In adult female birds there is but one ovary and oviduct, the left. In an early embryonic stage the right ovary and duct is present but these almost entirely disappear before hatching. Here is another of the countless weight-saving adaptations found in birds. The logic of this arrangement is confused, as biological facts often are, by a contradictory exception: as many as half the females of some species of hawks have both right and left ovaries.

Of the huge number of tiny ova enclosed in the membranous follicles of the surface of the ovary, only a few ripen at breeding time. These accumulate the huge yolks typical of

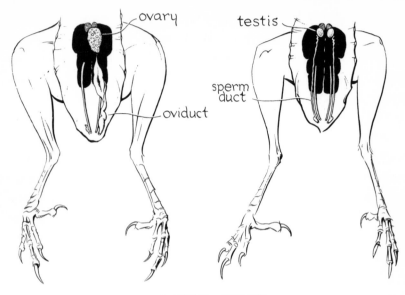

INACTIVE PERIOD

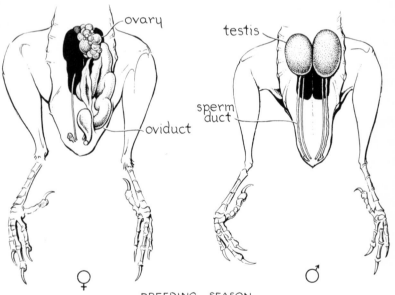

♀   ♂

BREEDING SEASON
HOUSE SPARROW (actual size)

the bird and reptile egg. When ripened, an ovum bursts from its follicle (Latin for small bag) and is caught up by the funnel-like entrance of the oviduct. It moves down this tube by the combined action of longitudinal muscles and the cilia that cover the inside surface of the duct. Albumen, formed by glands in the midsection of the oviduct, is deposited around the yolk. Shell membranes and shell are added in the uterus.

During coitus the hindmost part of the cloaca is turned outward and held together by both male and female. The male reproductive cells, the sperm, are ejected directly into the female cloaca and move up the oviduct. There, just one of the thousands of sperm will fertilize each descending ovum before the albumen, membranes, and shell are deposited around it.

The sexual organs, or gonads, of both male and female birds are small and inactive for the greater part of the year. Externally the cloaca of both sexes is well nigh indistinguishable. With the coming of the breeding season the testes of the male and the ovary and oviduct of the female enlarge greatly. The sexual organs of house sparrows weigh hundreds of times more during the breeding season than they do at other times. Here again is shown the tendency of birds to throw overboard every last bit of weight that is not necessary by losing most of the weight of their sex organs during the greater part of the year.

The Bird Brain

It is not within the scope of this book or the ability of its authors to delve very deeply into the indescribable complexities of the nervous system of any backboned animal. An outline of its structure and function and of the differences between the bird's brain and that of other vertebrates, however, will be a big help in understanding the living bird.

An internal system of communication and organization is a basic necessity for any animal. In single-celled animals the cell itself receives sensations and reacts to them; in all animals with bodies made up of many cells there is a distinct nervous system composed of cells specialized for receiving and reacting to various stimulations from both the external

sense organ (receptor)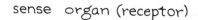

and internal environment. In its simplest form, the basic pattern of the nervous system is the same for all vertebrates. It can be thought of in two parts or sections, the central and the peripheral nervous systems. The central nervous system consists of the brain and the spinal cord; the peripheral consists of the afferent and efferent nerves. When the sense organs, or receptors, are stimulated, the afferent nerves pick up the stimuli and transmit them to the

afferent nerve

central nervous system

·sociation nerves

central system. There they are coordinated and analyzed. Responses to them are then sent out from the central system by way of the efferent nerves to the muscles and glands, causing them to act appropriately in response to the stimulation of the sense organs.

The special cells of the nervous system are the neurons. A typical neuron consists of a cell body with its several dendrites and a single axon. The end of the axon away from the cell body separates into fine fibrils. An axon may be several feet long in large animals, but re-

efferent nerve

muscle (effector)

dendrites

cell body

axon

sheath

gardless of length it is part of a single cell. A nerve consists of one or more neurons.

The nature of the nerve impulse is not fully understood. It does flow along the axon in the manner of an electric current and can be detected and measured by sensitive instruments. When the impulse reaches the axon fibrils, which intertwine with the dendrites of the next neuron, it jumps the gap, or synapse, after only an infinitesimal delay. Thus it proceeds from neuron to neuron. The speed of the nerve impulse is not fast when compared to that of electricity, however. In mammals, whose impulses generally travel the fastest, the greatest speeds amount to no more than 130 feet a second.

The visceral nervous system is a part of the peripheral system. The sensations it receives and the responses it makes are generally outside the realm of conscious control. The visceral system is subdivided into two parts: the visceral afferent system, which responds to stimuli from sensory cells in the internal organs — blood vessels, heart, etc.; and the visceral efferent, or autonomic, system, which stimulates the muscles of these organs and the glands. The autonomic system is in turn divided into two, the sympathetic and the parasympathetic systems. These differ as to their function and location. The sympathetic system speeds heart

axon fibrils

PERIPHERAL MOTOR NEURON

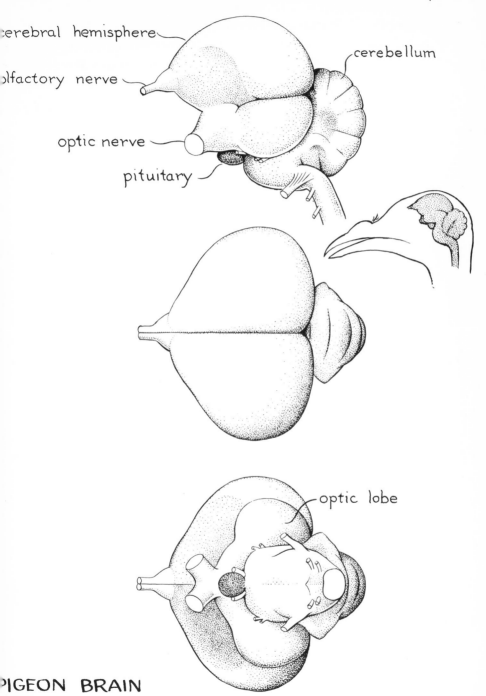

cerebral hemisphere

cerebellum

olfactory nerve

optic nerve

pituitary

optic lobe

PIGEON BRAIN

action, slows digestion, dilates the blood vessels of the muscles, and otherwise sets the body up for fight or flight. The parasympathetic system controls an exactly opposite effect. It slows heartbeat, speeds digestive processes, and so on. It prepares the body for rest, relaxation, and sleep. Many organs are, of course, enervated by both these systems.

The brain is a switchboard of fantastic complexity. Its various centers connect with various sets of nerve fibers and control the activities associated with them. In these centers the afferent impulses, or messages from the senses, are correlated, sorted, analyzed, and correct responses made to them by way of the efferent system. In the higher vertebrates there are also association centers whose job is memory and learning.

In spite of the slighting expression "bird brain," the bird's brain is proportionately larger than that of any of the vertebrates except mammals. The bird cerebellum is large and very well developed. It is connected with the control of movement, coordination, and posture so important to flying animals. The optic lobes are also large, an obvious connection with the need of birds for fine eyesight.

The cerebral hemispheres are by far the largest part of both the bird and mammal brain. However, the development of the cerebral hemispheres has gone off on an entirely different evolutionary direction in birds. The *corpus striatum* is a huge solid mass, and the cerebral cortex is relatively small — just the opposite of the proportions of the mammalian brain. The significance of this relationship can be found in the difference between the behavior of birds and mammals. Birds' activities are governed by the inherited and unlearned abilities we call instincts. Their learning ability is small compared to that of most mammals. They show little flexibility

in changing these inherited habits to meet conditions different from their usual way of life. On the other hand mammals, with their huge convoluted cerebral hemispheres, are
specialized for learned behavior and show great ability, cul-
minating in man, to meet altered situations with altered behavior.

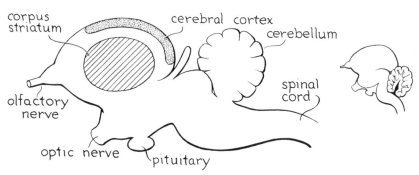

DIAGRAM OF BIRD BRAIN - BISECTED

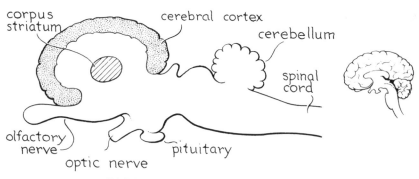

DIAGRAM OF MAMMAL BRAIN - BISECTED

Hormones

THERE ARE two principal types of glands in birds, as in the other vertebrates: those connected to other parts of the body by ducts, and those without ducts and releasing their products directly into the bloodstream. These latter are the endocrine glands, and their chemical products are the hormones. Hormones pour directly into the blood, spread throughout the entire body via the circulatory system, and profoundly affect its physical, chemical, and mental states. The endocrines are closely connected with the nervous system. They influence it and are influenced by it as well as by the internal and external environment. The endocrines act as a sort of chemical nervous system in that they serve the body as messengers. Moreover, they play a tremendously vital part in the processes of life itself. Some of the endocrines work independently, but many have interrelated activities of such extreme complexity that so far they have defied all except the smallest glimmer of understanding. There is recent evidence that the brain itself, as well as other parts of the nervous system down to a single neuron, may also secrete hormonal products. It is now appreciated that the hormones are not simple chemical messengers alone. They play a vital part in almost all, and possibly every, living process. Advances in the science of endocrinology are bringing us to the brink of new knowledge of enormous importance to the understanding of life.

Like the nervous system, the endocrine system had its beginning at the dawn of animal life. In the simplest multicellular animals there is a rudimentary nervous system and also a chemical system that foreshadow the complex nervous and endocrine functions of the higher animals.

Because both systems have such early origins in the history of life they are very similar in all vertebrates. The injection of identical synthetic sex hormones has much the same effect on a bird as on a mammal. Therefore a description of the location and influence of the most important known endocrine glands in birds will sound much like a description of the endocrine system in a dog or man. Work on the endocrine system has been predominantly medical and so is devoted to its function in humans, a few laboratory animals, and the useful domestic birds. Much less is known of its exact function in other birds.

The pituitary gland is located at the base of the brain. It has been called "the master mind of the endocrine system." The bird pituitary produces all the hormones known in the mammalian pituitary, with the possible exception of the growth hormone. These hormones not only act directly upon the body but also affect the function of other endocrine glands and the nervous system. Pituitary hormones influence the

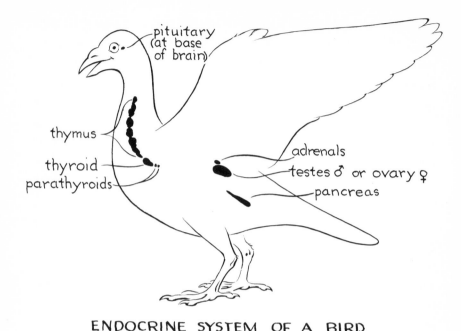

ENDOCRINE SYSTEM OF A BIRD

thyroid and adrenal glands and stimulate the gonads to produce their own hormonal products. A pituitary hormone (prolactin) stimulates the secretion of "pigeon's milk" and broodiness in birds in general. The same hormone is responsible for the production of milk in mammals. The artificial injection of prolactin in pigeons has the double effect of producing broodiness and causing the sexual organs to regress.

Birds can almost be considered sexless except during the mating season. In the winter the males of many species assume plumage very similar to that of the females. Other secondary sexual characteristics, such as song and territorial behavior, also disappear. Both the testes of the male and the oviduct of the female become reduced to a very small size, and the ovary produces no ripe eggs. At the proper season, under the influence of the changing amount of daylight and doubtless other environmental influences such as temperature in some cases, the pituitary produces the hormones that cause the gonads to enlarge, become active, and to produce sex hormones, androgen and estrogen, as well as mature sperm and ova. In the very early stages the embryo is neither male nor female — it contains all the potentials for the development of either sex. Hormones secreted by the embryonic gonads alone determine the sexual direction growth will take. The experimental introduction of male or female hormones into the growing embryo can bring about many degrees of sex reversal.

The adrenal glands are not divided into distinct zones in birds as they are in mammals, and little is known of the avian adrenal. However, proof that this gland manufactures several hormones vital to life has been demonstrated by removal of the gland — the birds die. Extracts from mammalian adrenals, it has been found, will maintain life in these birds. The hormone adrenaline has the same instantaneous effect of preparing an animal for fight or flight in birds as it has in mammals.

The paired thyroid gland lies beneath the trachea at the base of the neck. Its product, thyroxine, containing iodine, affects metabolism, growth, and sexual development. It also influences the growth rate, color, and structure of feathers and controls molting. Chickens develop goiters (enlarged thyroids) from a deficiency of iodine just as humans do.

There are four parathyroids attached to or near to the thyroid gland in chickens, ducks, pigeons, and doubtless other birds. They influence the formation of blood calcium and bone.

Glands located on the pancreas produce the hormone insulin; this controls the rate at which the body uses sugar. Grain-eating birds develop mild diabetic symptoms that disappear in about a week when these are removed. In contrast, a duck, when the glands are removed and it is fed entirely upon meat, develops severe symptoms. The carnivorous great horned owl dies from diabetes about a week after this operation is performed. However, in birds, unlike mammals, adrenal hormones apparently also play an important part in the regulation of sugar levels in the blood and tissues.

The thymus runs along the undersurface of the neck. This gland decreases in size with maturity and is sometimes completely absent in old birds. It is considered an endocrine gland but its removal has no observable ill effect and its function is open to question.

The hormone secretin influences the secretion of pancreatic juices. In mammals secretin is formed in the walls of the intestines, but it has been found only in the small intestine of birds.

The Ear

Upon looking through the microscope at a dissection of a pigeon ear we made for this book, a friend excitedly remarked, "But the semicircular canals really *are* semicircular!"

The bird ear, like that of most vertebrates, has two sensory jobs, one of balance as well as one of hearing. In ancestral fishes balance was the basic function of the ear. Hearing became more and more important as the vertebrates evolved. Both these senses are extremely well developed in birds.

The ear is divided into three areas, the outer, middle, and inner ears. The outer and middle ears function only to *receive* sound. The organs of equilibrium, along with those of actual hearing, lie deep within the inner-ear capsule. These structures are extremely complex in shape and almost defy verbal description. We shall depend upon the illustrations for this and limit the text to their function.

First, equilibrium. The membranous labyrinth is a closed

system of liquid-filled sacs and tubes encased in bone. In each of two sacs are oval spots, the utricular and saccular spots. A gelatinous substance covers sensory hairs on these. In the substance are calcium carbonate crystals collectively called an otolith (ear stone). As the head tilts the otolith presses more heavily on some hairs than on others. Information concerning the static tilt of the head in space is then relayed to the brain by branches of the auditory nerve connected to the sensory hairs of these balancing organs.

Information concerning *movement* is registered by means of the three semicircular canals, one for each dimension of space. Here too, sensory hairs are found in the bulblike end of each membranous canal. Movement in some way affects the liquid in the canals so that the hairs are stimulated and give information of the bird's position in and movement through space.

These structures of equilibrium are essentially the same in all vertebrates with the exception of a few primitive groups. They reached an evolutionary peak very early in the development of vertebrate life, and we all have inher-

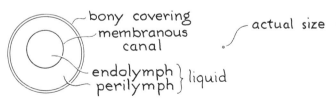

CROSS SECTION THROUGH A SEMICIRCULAR CANAL

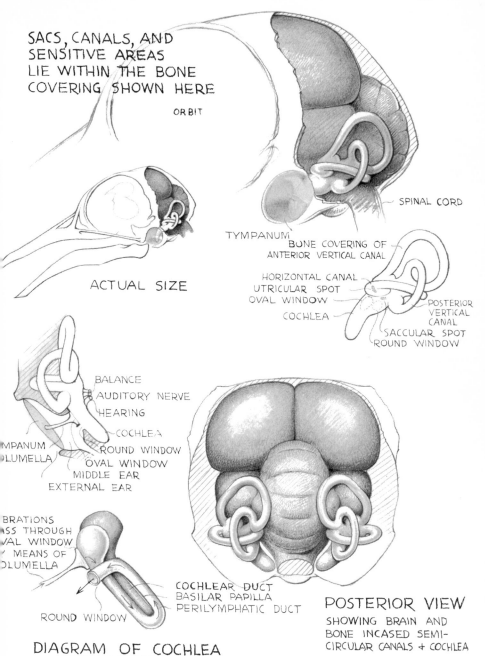

SACS, CANALS, AND
SENSITIVE AREAS
LIE WITHIN THE BONE
COVERING SHOWN HERE

ORBIT

ACTUAL SIZE

SPINAL CORD

TYMPANUM
BONE COVERING OF
ANTERIOR VERTICAL CANAL

HORIZONTAL CANAL
UTRICULAR SPOT
OVAL WINDOW
COCHLEA

POSTERIOR
VERTICAL
CANAL
SACCULAR SPOT
ROUND WINDOW

BALANCE
AUDITORY NERVE
HEARING
COCHLEA
ROUND WINDOW
OVAL WINDOW
MIDDLE EAR
EXTERNAL EAR

MPANUM
OLUMELLA

BRATIONS
SS THROUGH
VAL WINDOW
MEANS OF
OLUMELLA

ROUND WINDOW

COCHLEAR DUCT
BASILAR PAPILLA
PERILYMPHATIC DUCT

DIAGRAM OF COCHLEA
BONE COVERING REMOVED

POSTERIOR VIEW
SHOWING BRAIN AND
BONE INCASED SEMI-
CIRCULAR CANALS + COCHLEA

EAR OF A PIGEON

ited them. Subsequently there has been little necessity for change.

Hearing is a newer adaptation and the parts involved with it have become very elaborate in some classes. No birds have the external appendages used to collect and concentrate sound that are so decorative on many mammalian heads. The advantages of such hearing aids are obviously not great enough to offset the disadvantage of interrupting the smooth streamlining of the bird head.

In a pigeon, and most other birds, the opening of the external ear is covered by small feathers. It is hardly noticeable. The feathers are loosely textured and may be slightly raised when extra-keen hearing is necessary. In many animals the passage of the outer ear — the external meatus — is fairly long before it ends in the delicate membrane of the tympanum, or eardrum. In birds, however, this membrane is usually close to the outside of the skull. Beneath the tympanum, the middle ear is air-filled and has spaces that reach into the nearby areas of the skull. The eustachian tube leads from the middle ear to the pharynx. It aids in equalizing air pressure between the middle-ear cavity and the outside atmosphere.

Sound waves vibrate the tympanum and are conducted from it to the inner ear by the columella, which consists of cartilage and the stapes bone, which form a minute bit of abstract sculpture.

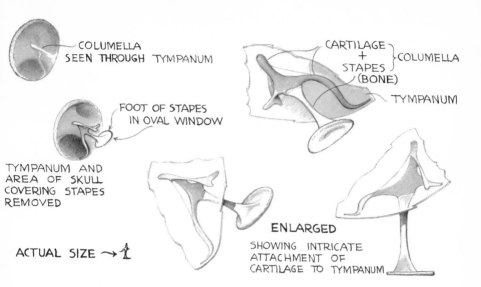

COLUMELLA
SEEN THROUGH TYMPANUM

CARTILAGE
+
STAPES } COLUMELLA
(BONE)

TYMPANUM

FOOT OF STAPES
IN OVAL WINDOW

TYMPANUM AND
AREA OF SKULL
COVERING STAPES
REMOVED

ACTUAL SIZE →

ENLARGED

SHOWING INTRICATE
ATTACHMENT OF
CARTILAGE TO TYMPANUM

LEFT COLUMELLA OF A PIGEON

Birds, mammals, and, among the reptiles, crocodiles, have greatly improved their hearing by the development of the cochlea in the inner ear. The cochlea has three parts, the fluid-filled perilymphatic duct, the cochlear duct, and the basilar papilla. The bulblike end of the perilymphatic duct presses against the foot of the stapes at the oval window. From here it forms an elongated loop that encircles the cochlear duct and the basilar papilla, sandwiched between the two. The perilymphatic duct then leads back to the middle ear, where it ends at the membrane-covered round window. The basilar papilla is the sensory organ of hearing and contains sensory cells connected to the brain by the auditory nerve. It is separated from the fluid-filled perilymphatic duct by a thin membrane only.

In hearing, the tympanum is made to vibrate by sound waves. The vibrations are transmitted across the middle ear by the columella. At the oval window the vibrations pass into the fluid of the perilymphatic duct, where they move past the sensory cells of the basilar papilla and stimulate them through the thin membrane. From these the auditory nerve carries the information to the brain. The actual sound waves, now in the form of vibrations in the fluid of the perilymphatic duct, are swept back to the middle ear through the round window and dissipate.

As we have said, the vibrations of airborne sound are transferred from the eardrum to the inner ear by the mechanical vibrations of the columella. Since the area of the eardrum is large and that of the footplate of the columella at the oval window small, the force of the vibrations is amplified. The larger the drum area in proportion to the footplate the greater is the amplification and auditory sensitivity. Small birds generally have large eardrums in relation to the size of their columella's footplate. Their entire ear also tends to be large in relation to the size of their bodies. The eardrums of larger birds are generally smaller in proportion to the footplate area. Owls, which have proportionately huge eardrums, are an exception to this rule.

Many songbirds can hear sounds of as high a frequency as 20,000 cycles a second. Their greatest sensitivity is at 2000 to 3000 cycles. This performance compares closely to that of human ears. On the low side, birds can hear sounds as low as 50 cycles, while human ears can detect sounds of 16 cycles.

The songbird's ability to discriminate pitch, in keeping with the range of their song — 1000 to 10,000 cycles — also compares to that of a human. However, pigeons, whose voices have but a narrow range of pitch, have a correspondingly small ability to discriminate it.

In addition to being extremely large in owls, the eardrums vary in size and shape between the right and left ears of the individual bird. This asymmetry doubtless makes it easier for these birds to pinpoint the direction of sounds. Owls also are undoubtedly able to make use of the difference of the time of arrival of sound between each of their widely spaced ears, as well as the difference in the intensity of sound at each ear, for the location of their prey. There is no doubt that exceptional hearing is responsible for much of owls' ability to locate those small, squeaking animals of the night upon which they live. It has been found in experiments that barn owls can catch living prey successfully in absolutely dark rooms.

It is interesting to note that the alarm calls of some small birds are of such high frequency that animals with ears spaced as far apart as those of hawks, or bird watchers, cannot detect phase differences in the sound waves and so become confused as to the location of the call. Birds of the same species, with their narrowly spaced ears, can locate the call's position precisely of course.

The Eye

Superb sight is as typical a characteristic of the bird as is flight. The two go hand in hand. Fine visual perception is necessary for flight itself, and only in an intensely alive, flying animal could eyes such as those of most birds have developed.

In proportion to over-all size, birds' eyes are much larger than the eyes of most mammals. Some species of owls and hawks have eyes actually larger than man's. The ostrich eye is two inches in diameter, the largest of any living land ani-

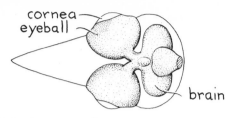

SPARROW (from underneath)

mal. Birds' eyes usually outweigh their entire brain, but since only the relatively small cornea shows through the lid opening, we do not realize how very large a bird's eye is until we see the entire eyeball in its huge orbit.

Light reflected from objects is received through a crystalline lens that concentrates and focuses it on the sensitive cells of the retina. The image cast upon the retina is upside down because of the manner in which light passes through a lens. This inversion is compensated for in the brain. The stimuli produced on the sensitive cells of the retina by light is sent to the brain through the fibers of the optic nerve.

The walls of the eyeball consist of three layers: the scleroid (hard) coat, outermost; the choroid (black, as on the inside of a camera) coat, in the middle; and the retina, innermost, which is made up of the light-sensitive cells, their accessory

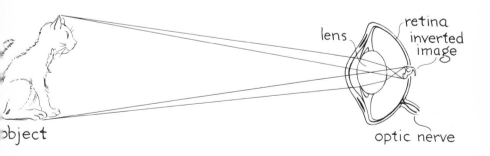

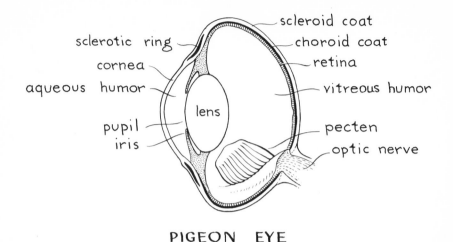

PIGEON EYE

cells, and nerve fibers. At the front of the eyeball the scleroid coat becomes the transparent cornea, which is fused to the skin lying over it. Behind the cornea is the lens, made up of crystal-clear onion-like layers of fine fibers. Around the lens edge the choroid and retinal layers fuse and expand into the ciliary body, which holds it in place. These layers also curve over the front of the lens to form the iris, which expands and contracts and automatically regulates the size of the pupil and controls the amount of light entering the eye. Between the lens and the cornea the cavities are filled with watery aqueous humor and, between the lens and the retina, with jellylike vitreous humor that supports the lens from behind.

In looking at objects at different distances the lens must change in some way in order to focus, or accommodate. In the camera this is accomplished by moving the lens backward toward the film for distant objects, or forward away from the film for near objects. In fishes, lampreys, and amphibians accommodation takes place in this same way. Birds, mammals, and reptiles accommodate by changing the shape of the lens, which in its at-rest condition is comparatively flattened and adjusted for faraway objects. Birds, and most reptiles, accommodate for near vision by means of the greatly developed ciliary body, which, ringlike, squeezes the lens and bulges it into a more spherical shape. Simultaneously other ciliary muscles contract and give the cornea greater curvature so that it too plays a part in accommodation. Mammals accomplish the same thing in a somewhat different way.

Visual sensitivity and visual acuity are two different qualities of seeing. Sensitivity is the degree to which an eye can see in weak light. Acuity is the degree to which an eye can see clearly, separately, and sharply the details of an object.

In the retina are two types of light-sensitive cells, rods and cones. Rods, because of their physical connections and chemical nature, have great sensitivity and comparatively small acuity. With cones the situation is reversed. Rods, however, are color-blind and give only black and white vision. Thus it is very difficult to see color in dim light. The cones do give color vision, and all evidence, physiological and psychological, points to the fact that most birds see color in more or less the same way as man. The cones of many birds, however, contain colored oil droplets, which modify color

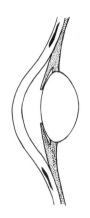

distant vision

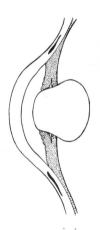

near vision

ACCOMMODATION IN A BIRD

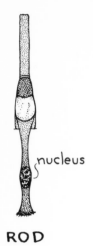

nucleus

ROD

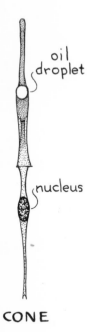

oil
droplet

nucleus

CONE

vision by acting as color filters. In pigeons the cells in the lower part of the retina contain yellow and in the upper an excess of red droplets. As the visual image is inverted, the yellow droplets come into play in scanning the sky, and their filter effect makes flying objects, like hawks, stand out against the blue with greater contrast. The red droplets function in the same way for objects seen with the upper retinal area against the green of fields or trees. The kingfisher has an excess of red droplets throughout its retina which aid in cutting down the glare and dazzle from water. Many other species have various colors and placement of oil droplets ranging from yellow through orange, red, and in some very pale green. Droplets of all these colors also aid in filtering out blue light, which is the most highly scattered by mist and dust, and give better vision of distant objects.

Various groups of birds have very different proportions and distribution of rods and cones in their retinas. Birds active by day, as might be expected, have large numbers of cones and relatively few rods. The small house sparrow has 400,000 cones per square millimeter in the central retinal areas. This density gives its eyes

red droplets

yellow
droplets

tremendous acuity as well as great ability to
detect the slightest movement. The hawk *Buteo
buteo* has 1,000,000 cones per square millimeter,
three times greater than the cone density in the
retina of man.

Rods predominate in the retinas of nocturnal
birds. This reduces acuity and color perception but increases the sensitivity to the very
weak light in which they move. Many other
nocturnal animals have eyes so lacking in acuity that other senses, such as smell or hearing,
have become more important than sight in
locating the exact position of an object. Their
tremendously sensitive rod-rich eyes remain as
detectors of movement. The flightless kiwi, the
most nocturnal bird, has a degenerate eye and,
perhaps unique among birds, a well-developed
sense of smell. Nocturnal bug hunters, such as
the whip-poor-will, do not have the acuity necessary to pick their small prey accurately from
the air as does a swallow, and must gather their
food by flying along with open, extra-wide,
gaping bewhiskered mouths.

But fast-moving creatures like birds must
have a comparatively greater minimum degree
of acuity than earthbound animals, which
move more slowly. Nocturnal or diurnal, a
flying creature must see well enough to be able
to maneuver at high speed. Even birds most
adapted to darkness have extra-slender tightly
packed rods. So, while an owl's eyes have
about ten times more sensitivity than those of

**1,000,000
CONES
PER
SQ. MM.**

central area and
fovea

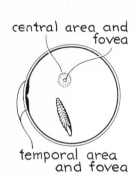

temporal area
and fovea

HUMMINGBIRD

central area and
fovea

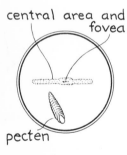

pecten

GULL

the day-living mammal man, they also have a much greater degree of acuity than the night-living mammal *Tarsius*.

In many vertebrate retinas there is an area of densely packed cones from which rods are excluded. This is the location of acutest vision. In the retinas of many birds, and some lizards, there are two such areas. The central area (area centralis) is located in more or less the optical center of the eye. The second, the temporal area, lies toward the rear outside margin of the retina. The species possessing the two areas — such as the hummingbird in the illustration — have a central area of acute vision to use when looking outward at right angles to the body, and the temporal area of acute vision for use when looking ahead. Diverse birds of wide-open spaces, from herring gull to ostrich, have central areas in the shape of long horizontal bands to suit the form of their landscape and reduce the necessity for eye and head movement to bring the area of acute vision into use.

Within the central area of many birds there is a well-developed depression with convex sides, the fovea. It occupies the tissue of the retina only and does not displace any visual cells. This layer is, of course, transparent and has a different refractive index (light-bending power) from the vitreous humor. When light passing through the vitreous strikes the convex sides of the foveal depression its rays are bent

outward, magnifying the image at this point.
Gordon Walls, from whose remarkable book
The Vertebrate Eye much of the material in this
chapter has been drawn, calculates that the
magnification can amount to as much as 30 per
cent in area and further increases the visual
acuity of the central area within which it is
located.

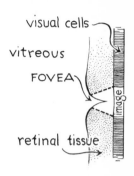

In hawks, eagles, terns, swallows, shrikes,
kingfishers, and similar birds, a fovea occurs in
both the central and temporal areas. These
birds are all hunters, and the eyes are placed
forward in their heads so that to a comparatively great extent they look frontward with
overlapping binocular vision. In diurnal birds
the fovea is deep and well developed. In owls
and in species long domesticated it is poorly
developed or entirely absent.

Birds such as ducks and songbirds have eyes
placed very much on the side of the head and
therefore look outward more than forward.

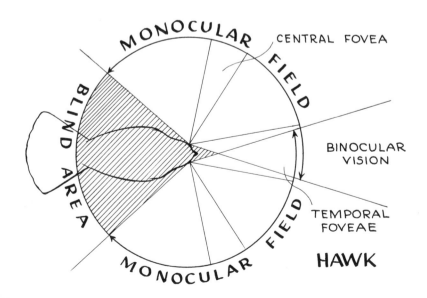

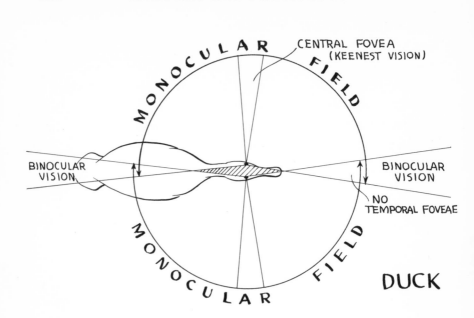

Here there is but one area and one fovea. Head movement is very noticeable in these birds as they bring this area into play. All bird eyes fit tightly and are almost immovable in the orbit, so that the head must be turned to point the center of the eye at an object. We have all noticed that chickens constantly cock their heads when looking at anything they want to see especially well. This head-cocking motion has given the robin a reputation of listening for worms. The bird is only bringing the central area of one eye or another into play in spotting the glint of the worm among the grasses. Turning its head at 90 degrees to its body, so that it can look ahead with the eye center, is a wasteful effort. Consequently the robin turns its head only slightly, spots a shining meal, and hops off in that direction. Then it may cock its other eye at the same angle, see another worm, and hop off at right angles to its first direction. Thus a robin's course across the lawn is often zigzag. If you chart this course you will see how much a bird depends on the central area of its eyes.

Extremes in the placement of the bird eye are found in woodcocks and bitterns. Bitterns habitually camouflage themselves by pointing their long necks and heads straight upward and freezing. With the help of very fine protective coloration, when in this position they closely resemble the reeds among which they live. As this behavior takes place at times of great danger, good vision is particularly important. So the bittern's eyes are placed low on the side of its head. With bill pointing to the sky, this bird can look under its chin and see all that goes on in front of it.

The woodcock feeds by poking its long flexible bill deep into the ground for worms. In this position a bird cannot move its head or, with normally placed eyes, see anything in front of it but the ground. The woodcock's eyes are toward the back and well up on its head in order for the bird to use them at this dangerous moment of immobility. The area of binocular overlap is greater backward than frontward. The woodcock literally has eyes in the back of its head.

The shape of the bird eyeball is not spherical as in man. The section containing the lens and cornea bulges forward and is contained by a ring of bony plates, the sclerotic ring, found

chicken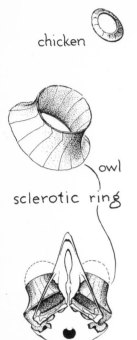

owl

sclerotic ring

GREAT HORNED OWL
(from underneath)

only in birds, certain fishes, and reptiles. The shape of the sclerotic ring varies greatly in different groups of birds. Notice how deep it is in the owl eye compared to the shallow saucer-shaped ring of the chicken.

Within this over-all shape of the avian eye there are three main subdivisions — flat, globose, and tubular eyes. Flat-eyed birds include the vast majority of all species. The flat eye has a large retina in comparison to the size of the lens and its axis is shorter than its diameter. This furnishes the wide field of vision needed by birds that search for their food on the ground or among the trees and bushes.

Species with globose eyes are the predators that require great acuity at long distances, and wing-feeding insect eaters. In these birds the increased distance of the lens from the retina, because of the lengthened axis, throws the image of a smaller field over a larger portion of the light-sensitive surface. This brings a greater number of cells into play in seeing a given object. For example, if two small objects are close together at a great distance, the image of both may stimulate but one tiny spot on the wide-angle retina of a sparrow's flat eye. The two objects will not be resolved and will appear

FLAT

GLOBOSE

TUBULAR

distance from lens to retina in flat eye

few cells
stimulated

many cells
stimulated

distance from lens to retina in globose eye

as one. But in the globose eyes of a hawk the light from these
two images will be spread over a greater area of retina and
thus stimulate more light-sensitive cells, clearly resolving
images of both objects. This is the so-called telescopic power
of the eyes of birds of prey — actually a matter of bringing a
greater number of visual cells into use in covering a certain
visual area. Just as every advantage in life seems to have an
accompanying disadvantage, so with globose eyes, which cannot cover as wide a field as do flat eyes.

The tubular eyes of some eagles are really of the globose
type in that they are a more extreme adaptation of the same
tendency and bring even greater resolving power. The axis
of these eyes is longer than that of the globose, resulting in
an even greater distance between lens and retina.

The situation in the tubular eyes of owls is an entirely different story. In these nocturnal birds the lens-cornea section
of the eye has become relatively enormous in order to collect
and concentrate all possible light. The size of this section
has evolved to be so big that any feasible bird skull could not
possibly hold a retina of normal proportion to the lens. So
the back part of the owl eye has become reduced in area and

this causes the tubular shape. However, the owl lens is set comparatively far back and is quite spherical, like a wide-angle camera lens. This results in a small but complete image, fitting the available retinal space. Thus a wide retina is not required to cover a comparatively wide field. The telescopic effect of the globose and the eagle-type tubular eye is not present in the tubular owl eye, which is adapted for greatly concentrating light over a small retinal area. This same modification is present in many other dark-living animals, which include the mammals *Galago*, *Tarsius*, a few other primitive primates, and many deep-sea fishes.

Even though the owl retina has become reduced in size the eyeball is crammed so tight in its orbit that it is even more immobile than the eyes of most other birds. To compensate, these birds have developed extra-flexible necks and can turn their heads through an arc of 270 degrees — or almost all the way around. They can make this motion so quickly that the small-boy legend has arisen that an owl's head simply goes round and round, revolving on its neck, and will twist entirely off if one continues to circle one of these birds long enough.

Birds along with other vertebrates, except most fishes and snakes, have opaque upper and lower eyelids. Birds, many reptiles, and some mammals have a third eyelid, the nictitating (winking) membrane. There is a remnant of the nictitans in humans at the lower inside corner of the eye. In birds this membrane has varying degrees of transparency. When drawn across the cornea it protects the eye and at the same time allows the bird to see. It also cleans and aids in keeping the cornea moist. Most birds blink entirely with the nictitans and close their true eyelids only in sleep.

A most remarkable organ protrudes into the vitreous humor from where the head of the optic nerve enters the eyeball. It is peculiar to birds but homologous to the papillary cone of reptiles. This, the pecten, has to be seen to be appreciated.

The pecten is highly vascular. Its convoluted

PECTEN OF A DOMESTIC FOWL

PECTEN OF AN OSTRICH

cross section
showing blood vessels

surface, ephemeral in delicacy, gives it a large surface area in a small space, like a radiator. Some birds, such as ostriches, have pectens of a different form—with flat radiating vanes. What the pecten is for no one really knows. Since it consists largely of small blood vessels

cross section

it undoubtedly serves as an organ of nourishment to supply the high metabolic needs of the bird retina. These needs are greater for cones than for rods. Generally those birds with cone-rich eyes have larger pectens, possessing more folds, than those in whose eyes rods predominate.

But the peculiar form of the organ has led many to insist that it must have some additional function. The most reasonable theory as to its use states that the pecten aids in detecting motion as it casts its shadow on the retina. Just those birds requiring the greatest perception of motion have the best-developed pectens. However, these same species also have the greatest retinal metabolic requirements, which, as explained above, could also cause great pecten development. There are valid objections to all of the many other theories about the pecten. The use of this unique organ remains one of the greatest mysteries peculiar to the bird eye.

Flight

To AID THE understanding of flight, air can be considered as a fluid. Like a fluid, air has weight. The ocean of air that surrounds the earth is fifty or sixty miles thick and considerable pressure is developed. At sea level this atmospheric pressure is 14.7 pounds per square inch.

The bird and the airplane use the same basic forces to lift themselves into the air. The explanation of this ability is

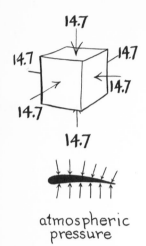

atmospheric
pressure

dynamic pressure

![airfoil with arrows]

atmospheric
pressure
plus
dynamic pressure

found in the shape of the wing and the manner in which air flows around it when it moves.

The ideal wing has a streamlined cross section that is flattened on the underside. Thus, from front to rear, the curved upper surface is longer than the more flattened under one. When air flows around the moving wing, that which travels over the longer upper surface must move faster than that traveling past the shorter under-surface. This moving air creates new pressure at these wing surfaces in addition to the ever present atmospheric pressure. This new pressure is proportionate to the speed at which the air is moving past the wing, and exerts its force in a backward direction to produce drag. The shape of the wing causes the air to move past the upper surface faster than at the undersurface. Greater moving (dynamic) pressure therefore is created at the upper surface.

However, and this is the crux of the matter, the *total* of dynamic pressure and atmospheric pressure is always the same, or is constant. The greater the dynamic pressure, the less the atmospheric pressure. As the dynamic pressure is greater at the top surface of the wing, the atmospheric pressure must be less there. At the bottom surface, where the dynamic pressure is less, the atmospheric pressure is greater.

If there is greater pressure under a wing than over it, the direction of the resulting force *must be up*. This force is the wing lift (sometimes called top-surface lift), which explains how a bird or a plane defies gravity. It is simple to produce this effect yourself. Hold a thin piece of paper in your hands, as in the illustration. Blow gently over its upper surface to speed up the flow of air there; this increases the dynamic pressure and decreases the atmospheric pressure. The edge away from you will rise, demonstrating the principle of top-surface lift.

While lift is forcing the wing — and the attached bird — upward, the dynamic pressure is causing drag and forcing it backward. The total effect, or resultant force, is therefore in an upward and backward direction. This is not helpful in moving the bird ahead. The old-fashioned airplane overcomes drag by means of its propeller.

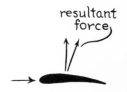

The bird also moves forward by means of a propeller. The bird prop is contained in the "hand" section and the primary feathers attached to it; the arm section continues to maintain lift. During the powerful downstroke of flapping flight, the leading edge of this hand part of the wing is held lower than the trailing edge. It cuts downward and forward in an arc. If we reconstruct the above diagram of resultant forces under these conditions, we find that the resultant force is now upward and forward.

The details of just how a bird applies these basic principles during its flight are so complex that it would take many lifetimes of devoted investigation to fathom them all. However, high-speed and motion-picture photography and aerodynamic research with the aid of its tool the wind tunnel and smoke stream have revealed a good many secrets. Flight has puzzled mankind until just a few years ago, simply because we could not see "fast" enough to figure out what happened when a bird whirred by. Photography has enabled us to see the wing during its fastest motion and the smoke stream has enabled us to see the moving air. Bird flight is much more easily analyzed with the unaided eye when the mechanics of it are understood, because one then knows what to look for. Such knowledge adds no end to the entrancing occupation of watching birds as they go about their airy business.

So far we have discussed the wing only when it is held parallel to the direction in which it is moving. The lift of a wing can be added to by increasing its angle to the direction of the flow of air. When this "angle of attack" is increased the air stream is deflected downward and exerts additional pressure against the underwing surface, adding to the lift described above. This extra lift is about proportional to the increase in angle; but when the angle of attack becomes too great the air stream will no longer smoothly follow the top surface of the wing. A turbulent eddy then appears. This destroys the top-surface lift. As top-surface lift is by far the most important of the two pressures responsible for flight, a wing at this angle becomes ineffective. This is the stalling angle.

The angle before which stalling will occur in a given wing can be increased somewhat by the use of "slots." If a small winglet is placed just ahead of the wing, a stream of air is squeezed through the resulting space, or slot. The constriction speeds up this air and smooths out the flow over the top surface, re-establishing top-surface lift. Birds have various slotting devices.

In ordinary forward flight the feathers of the alula are held tight against the leading edge of the wing so that it blends with and functions as a part of the whole. When the stalling angle is reached the alula is spread forward at the thumb joint to become an effective slot.

Slotted wingtips are made possible both by the bird's ability to spread the first few primaries apart, as you might spread the fingers of your hand, and by the special shape of these feathers in many bird wings. The primaries, particularly the first few, have a narrower vane at the outer part than at the inner, or are emarginated. The first primary, socketed in the terminal bone of the index finger, is espe-

SLOTTING

slots open

tail down

cially movable and is deeply emarginated in many species. The stalling angle is most often reached during landing and take-off. It is at these times that slotting in both wingtip and alula is most noticeable.

Another method of increasing lift comes from the use of flaps. In planes a movable section of the trailing edge of the wing is lowered to increase the angle of attack at this point only. In birds the tail is spread and lowered to function in a similar manner. Increasing the angle of attack of the entire wing for this purpose would result in a stall, but by spreading and lowering its tail a bird is able to slow its flight without stalling.

Increase in speed gives added top-surface lift equal to the square of the extra speed. The wings of a bird that has doubled its speed will supply four times the lift. So, fast-flying birds can have small wings and use low angles of attack. The fastest jet planes can have almost no wings at all.

The shape of the wing affects the type of flight of which the bird is capable as well as its over-all efficiency. There is a tendency for the stream of air flowing under the wing to whirl up over the trailing edge and upset the all-important flow over the upper surface. This effect is particularly troublesome at the wing-tips. The most efficient wing, aerodynamically speaking, is one that is long enough to keep the wingtip disturbances far apart and not so narrow as to permit the turbulence at the trailing edge from creeping over too much of the top surface. A wing answering these requirements is long and narrow, like those of an albatross. But pure aerodynamic efficiency (the expenditure of the least energy for the most flight) does not necessarily fit the kind of wings needed for certain types of flight.

Long wings are structurally weak and require proportionately more muscle power than short ones. We find a wide variation in the shapes of wings of different groups of birds according to the requirements of the environment in which they live. The short, broad, rounded wings of a pheasant are suited to powerful bursts of ascending flight through thickets and trees. Unfortunately they are relatively inefficient and require tremendous amounts of energy. A pheasant cannot sustain flight for long without resting. On the other hand, the long wings of the albatross permit these birds of the open sea to remain airborne for long periods with a minimum of energy expended. Albatross wings, nevertheless, are comparatively weak and operate efficiently only at high speeds. The birds have great difficulty in taking off from land or sea. Their wings are so long that they would be a liability in any but the most open windy places. An albatross would be as helpless in a brushy upland as a pheasant over the reaches of the ocean. The wings of most birds are a compromise between these two extremes, an adaptation that enables each species to lead its particular way of life.

As we have said, the forward propulsion in bird flight has its source in the propeller action of the hand section of the wing. In level flight the wing moves downward-forward and upward-backward. The wingtips move through an arc and travel farther and faster than the arm section. In addition

to the over-all propeller function of the hand section, each
of the first few primaries works as a small separate propeller.
In the downstroke these primaries are separated and spread.
The leading edge of each is rotated downward and assumes
the proper propeller pitch and twist as the air pressure

changes its design during different moments of the stroke.

The up, or recovery, stroke is a complex movement that
completes the "revolution" of the bird propeller. It starts
in the arm section shortly before the hand section has completed the downstroke. The primaries are then dragged upward as the wrist bends. The arm completes the recovery
stroke while the primaries are still bent down, since it does
not have so far to travel. The stroke is completed as the primaries catch up with the arm in a rapid snap that is often a
blur of motion even in very fast photographs. In the recovery
stroke the primaries may be rotated in an opposite angle to
that of the downstroke. At the start they are widely separated, allowing air to pass freely through them. During the
final snap the primaries come together, overlap, and, because
their angle is still reversed, aid in pushing the bird forward.
In other words, the bird propeller becomes a pusher on the

A PRIMARY AS
A PROPELLER

upstroke and eliminates some of the interruption in the smooth flow of power that results from birds not having a rotary propeller. While both the down and recovery strokes are taking place, the arm section bearing secondary feathers acts as a wing proper, maintains lift, and stabilizes flight.

The marvelous adaptations that have enabled the slender primary feathers to serve as propellers can be changed on the instant as the bird flattens the angles of the wing, draws the primaries together, and glides. Maneuverability can be controlled with wondrous efficiency as the function of the individual wing is changed. Birds often continue the full, flapping stroke of one wing while bracing or folding the other to make quick turns. At times the entire body as well as the spread tail aids in steering, braking, and working as a flap. By changing the characteristic of the wing the bird can fly at slow, medium, or fast speeds with equal efficiency. Flaps can be lowered, angles changed, slots opened or closed, or prop angles and pitch adjusted. When all is done and the bird is at rest, long wings can be neatly folded away. The flight of an airplane is a crude and simple performance compared to that of a bird and requires stabilizing devices that the bird does not need. The only superiority in flight that we have been able to master is one of overwhelming speed and altitude.

Taking off is a difficult moment for many birds just as it is for planes. Some species cannot rise from a standstill at all except under favorable conditions. Gannets, for instance, can only rise from the surface of the water by launching themselves from the tops of waves in a spanking breeze, and they are unable to fly up from level land except against very strong winds. However, gannets live and nest on high cliffs, from which they launch themselves in a downward glide that develops enough speed to give the required lift.

Condors, whose wings are long and broad, can be caught within small fenced areas. When bait is placed in these "traps" the great birds land and feed. There simply is not enough runway in which to develop enough speed for take-off when they are ready to leave.

Birds with proportionately small wings cannot develop enough lift until a fairly high rate of air speed has been reached. Coots, swans, and many geese must take long, splattering runs over the surface of the water to gain speed for take-off, as do the diving and sea ducks.

Birds ordinarily land so effortlessly that it is hard to comprehend the extreme difficulty of an act appearing so simple. The bird must come in fast enough to maintain lift and yet land accurately, gently, and surely, perhaps on a slender twig swaying in the wind. It must often do this with wings in awkward positions from the interference of intervening branches.

When landing, birds must use every flight resource they possess, in an almost magical exhibition of nervous and muscular control.

The bird comes whisking in at full flying speed. The next instant it may be straining to brake with every faculty, wings cupped overhead as parachutes, feet forward, tail lowered and spread — even its body seems flattened to present every possible bit of surface to the resisting air. Then the perch may move in the wind. So quickly that it seems almost simultaneous, the bird is flying again with driving primaries and lifting wings. Perhaps its body is angled, one wing beating and the other stretched and braced for a pivot in a turn that must be made in a flash. In the next smallest moment of time it is braking again. Suddenly the bird is on the perch, safe and nonchalant, with folded wings. Even with modern electronic flash photography, which can freeze the action of any bird with fantastically short exposures, it is impossible to analyze more than an outline of all the things that happen during such a flying performance. Every muscle, every bone, every feather is in a constantly changing synchronization of blurred motion that may well be the height of purely physical achievement possible for any backboned animal.

Many birds can fly vertically for a short distance at least. Edgar Queeny tells, in his fine book *Prairie Wings*, of photographing a mallard that rose straight up for a hundred feet, flew backward for some distance, and then turned and continued normal flight.

In vertical flight the wingbeats are parallel to the ground. The wing functions entirely as a propeller with all lift directed upward, its feathered blades working in principle as do those of a helicopter. Hovering is accomplished in the same manner. No matter what the angle of the bird's body may be, the wings beat backward and forward, parallel to the ground.

Hummingbirds are expert hoverers and can readily fly backward by adjusting the angle of the primaries in reverse. Their wings are small, with a very short arm section that rotates freely at the shoulder joint. Actually the wings are almost entirely propeller. Such a wing is inefficient aerodynamically and requires great energy in flight, but energy is just what a hummingbird has in copious quantities. Its tiny wings are very efficient for its special sort of flight.

In ordinary flight the downstroke is more powerful than the recovery, although in hovering the recovery plays a greater part and must be more nearly equal to the down, or in this case forward, stroke in power. It is interesting in this respect to note that the minor pectoral muscle of hummingbirds is more nearly equal to their major pectoral in size.

All flying birds can glide for at least a short distance. Soaring, or sustained flight without apparent movement of the wings, is peculiar to some groups. Among these are eagles, hawks, vultures, gulls, albatrosses, and many other sea birds. The common turkey vulture seems gently suspended by some invisible support as it soars overhead or disappears into the distance on set wings. In fact an unseen force is exactly what is keeping this beautiful — at a distance at least — bird in the sky.

Air is in continual movement. Not only does the wind blow parallel to the ground but currents rise obliquely or directly upward, sometimes to great heights. The causes of these movements of air are many. Obstructions such as mountainsides, shorelines, and buildings deflect wind up or down. The land absorbs or reflects different amounts of heat according to its texture. A bare patch of sand, a highway, or a plowed field will heat air more quickly than nearby grassland or forest and will send columns of warm air upward. When a bird soars it is really gliding downward within the confines of a column of air that is rising as fast or faster than the bird is dropping. It is like stepping slowly downward on an escalator that is going up. This type of flight is called thermal soaring. Very often the shape of the rising column can be seen by observing the outline traced by the circling bird. It is illuminating to compare this pattern with that of the land below. The "flyingest" sort of flying a human can perform is that of the silent, graceful gliders or sail planes making use of these same forces.

The surface of the sea is smooth compared to that of the land. The surface texture of water varies little. There are few rising columns of heated air, and deflected air currents from

waves are effective only at very low heights. Soaring or gliding over the empty sea is quite a different performance from
overland soaring. The energy utilized is obtained from the
velocity of the wind blowing at different speeds at different
distances above the surface. Frictional drag causes the wind
to blow more slowly near the water than at slightly higher
altitudes. It gradually increases up to about fifty feet, where
full speed is reached.

The albatross, the largest flying bird — with a wingspread
up to twelve feet — exploits this phenomenon in a regular
and methodical way that can be continued over long periods.
Energy used by the bird itself is so small that the albatross
and other soaring sea birds can often follow ships for days.
Let's start with the albatross gliding at high speed in a downwind direction close to the surface of the sea. With set wings
the bird now turns into the wind and gains altitude. As it
rises its speed over the water (ground speed) drops rapidly.
But its speed through the air may actually increase, since the
wind velocity increases steadily as the bird rises. The albatross is extracting kinetic energy from the wind and storing it
away as potential energy in the form of altitude.

Having used this phenomenon to its fullest at about fifty
feet, where the speed of the wind levels off, the bird turns
downwind again. Away it sails, using gravity, the energy of
the wind behind it, plus the gradual decrease of wind velocity
to regain its air speed. It is now using the potential energy
of its altitude to gain speed. Of course, the bird eventually
runs out of altitude. It must turn again into the wind to regain potential energy in the form of height for use in another
downwind leg. Thus the bird can travel a mean distance forward only in a series of tacks. However, it can do this with
little more expenditure of its own metabolic energy than that

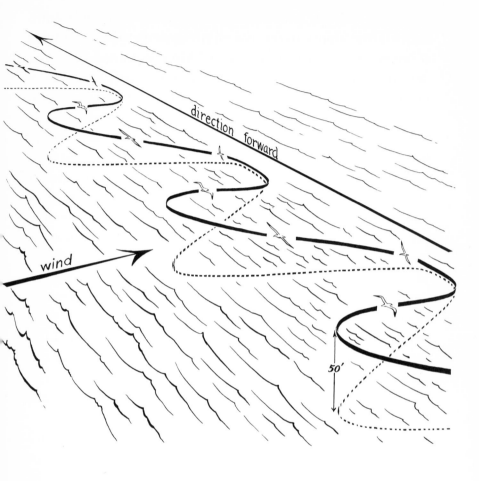

required to keep its wings set. The energy utilized to carry its body forward has been extracted from the wind. The albatross seems to be getting something for nothing.

Ships at sea create obstructions that form upward air currents in an otherwise level wind. Gulls and many other sea birds will follow a ship in this upcurrent for long stretches, scarcely needing to move a wing. Once, on the boat to Nantucket Island, we were standing in the stern exulting as always in the soaring being demonstrated by a crowd of herring gulls. Their ability to use the ship's updraft seemed to vary according to the age of the birds. Mottled young gulls got into difficulties occasionally, through some small unevenness in the flow of air or awkwardness of flight, and had to flap desperately to catch up again; but the mature white birds sailed on without a hitch. One fine flier, pure white, with soft gray mantle and brilliant yellow bill, was an outstandingly better performer than the younger birds. He glided along, seeming to feel the changes in the air before they happened with delicate pointed wingtips. Tiny adjustments, bracings, bendings, changes in angle, and extension of wing were all that were needed to keep him in even steady flight. He would reach out with hardly a flutter to pick from the air the bread we threw him. Once he very calmly tilted his beak upward, adjusted his wings to maintain balance, and reached forward with one webbed foot to give his itching chin a good scratching. Then he settled back without a break into his smooth soaring.

A comparison of the wings of the condor with those of the wandering albatross, both birds outstanding performers in their own types of soaring flight, shows differences in flying equipment that demonstrates the niceties of adaptation to special ways of life. The condor has an aspect ratio, or the proportion of wing's width to length, of moderate proportions.

That of the albatross may be as high as eighteen to one. The aspect ratio of the pigeon wing is about five to one. The wing loading, or weight of the bird in proportion to the area of its wing surface, is small in both the condor and the albatross. The condor's broad wings can be greatly slotted. Extreme emargination and flexibility of the primaries allows a large percentage of the wing to be slotted. The albatross wing is sharply pointed and cannot be slotted at all.

The reasons for these great differences in the wings of two species that both soar superbly is found in the speeds at which each performs and the type of air movement prevailing over their different habitats. The condor operates in rugged, broken mountains with a confused jumble of rising and falling air currents. It flies at slow speeds, requiring great angle of incidence and broad wings to maintain lift — therefore the slots to avoid stall. The slots of the condor wing can, however, be closed and the wing pointed, instantly changing the character of the wing. This versatility is useful among the erratic winds of mountain and valley.

The albatross, on the other hand, flies in air that blows more evenly. It flies at much higher speeds than does the condor. The albatross may average slightly more than 40 miles an hour. So, because of the fact that lift increases with the square of the speed, this bird does not need the added lift, extreme angle of attack, or the antistall slotting seen in the condor wing. On the other hand, an albatross cannot fly efficiently unless the wind is blowing at least three or four miles an hour. It has great difficulty in landing, on land or water, in a calm. Often it cannot take off at all at these times, especially from land. However, over the seas they haunt, a windless day is rare and the strongest gale does not discompose an albatross in the least. Robert Cushman Murphy says of the wandering albatross, *Diomedea exulans* (what a fitting name): "But when gales blow and heavy seas race past the anchorage, cooping a ship's crew on board, then the albatrosses fairly fill the air, and no blizzard, apparently, can be severe enough to stem their riotous enjoyment."

The speed of the flight of birds varies over a wide range. The great blue heron cruises sedately at about 20 miles an hour while the mallard bustles along at 40. Most of the small passerines operate between 20 and 30 during their peculiar undulating flight that is the result of several quick flaps, folded wings for an instant, and several more quick strokes. The swift may be the speediest bird, and has been clocked at well over 100 miles an hour in still air. A duck hawk has been reported as flying 175 miles per hour and sandpipers at 110. Recordings of the speed of individual performances do not mean a great deal unless all conditions under which the flight took place are known. A bird that is migrating may travel faster than one of the same species loafing about on home grounds. A bird trying to outspeed a hawk will naturally move faster than when flying from feeding grounds to nest. Conditions of wind and rising air can make great differences in the possible speed of bird flight.

As you watch a mob of gulls trifling easily with a blustering nor'wester, a hummingbird as it goes earnestly about its business among the blossoms, the flush of a ruffed grouse, bright warblers among the leaves, or the long purposeful flight of migrating waterfowl, you are seeing a supreme physical performance that is the sum of all this multitude of parts and happenings that we have been examining.

Epilogue: Bird and Man

REALISTIC THINKING about the natural sciences no longer isolates *any* living thing. There is no line between the "natural" world and the supposed "unnatural" world of man. As more is learned about all the processes of life it becomes more and more evident all life is an interrelated, interdependent whole that must be studied as a whole. We cannot truly know anything about birds unless we know something of insects, mammals, water, soil, weather—all aspects of the environment in general. We cannot, of course, learn anything about these without learning a good deal about ourselves in the bargain. And, as we come to know ourselves and our relationships to everything else, we come to realize our full dependence upon the rest of the world of life and, since we are humans who can control so much, its dependence upon us.

We can no longer look at nature as though we were special products of creation, set apart and separate from the fate of such others as birds. And with this new way of looking at the living world comes a new feeling of love for and oneness with all life. We hope that in talking about the bird we have given a little understanding of some of the principles of how and why this living world is interrelated — no great detail of the relationship itself, but the general processes behind it and how it came to be — an understanding that gives practical truth to the intuitive sentiments of nature lovers and to Albert Schweitzer's creed of reverence for life.

There is no longer, if there ever was, such a thing as "pure science" or an "ivory tower" scientist. The very meaning of the word science (from the Latin *scire*, to know), knowledge, the act of understanding, a clear perception of the truth, denies this traditional assumption. All truth, and thus all science in the true meaning of the word, is precious and useful for man's life. One of the newest of the biological sciences is ecology, the study of organisms as they are totally related to the environment. Environment, in this complete sense, is everything that affects whatever organism we are considering, including that organism itself and its own effect on the environment. Thus ecology is the study of everything that affects life on earth, and every study ends, in the last analysis, as an ecological study. So, being human, sooner or later we come to regard all organisms in their relation to us. This of course gives almost every biological investigation significance for the science of *human* ecology.

In what we are about to say regarding human ecology we may seem to be identifying ourselves with those often referred to as prophets of doom, people who cry that man has made a mess of things and may eliminate himself shortly. But many of those lumped in this group are not pessimists, nor are they speaking for the doubtful enjoyment of prophesying evil. These are the biologists, naturalists, conservationists, some political and social scientists, and psychologists who think in terms of life — men and women who believe in the mind of man, that indescribably awesome product of over two billion years of time, and have faith in his ability to solve his problems with this mind rather than submit to the vagaries of undirected forces; men and women who believe that the first step in solving any problem is to recognize it honestly.

No other living being has come nearly so close to controlling his environment as has man. Our intellectual power allied with our extreme individual and universal adaptability has enabled us to take over, use, and alter a tremendous portion of the earth. At the moment there is probably no place on earth where results of our activities are not felt and, if we are not wise and careful, we may end everything all at once in one glorious detonation or, more slowly, fatally affect the genetic future of all life.

Humans use the environment in a sense that can be applied to no other creature. By means of our domestic plants and animals and technology we have been able to extract a larger and ever larger share of the food-energy that moves in great cycles throughout the world of life. Much of this use of the environment has been rich and rewarding, but much of it has been destructive. We have not only used the environment, we have in many cases used it up. We have removed its potential fertility — its ability to support life of any form at anywhere near an optimum. We can look back at known records for seven thousand years and trace a dreary path of devastation that has followed waves of various civilizations; waves that have left poor blighted lands inhabited by poor blighted peoples in their wake. In the broad sense we are the most universally predatory species that has ever existed. We prey on wild creatures and plants standing in the way of our ceaseless quest for food-energy. We prey on the fertility of the earth as we extract its minerals and destroy its vital fabric with our crops, the destruction of our forests, and our grazing domestic herds. We squander in a few years the limited fossil fuel, coal, and oil, which are the accumulations of untold ages. We poison the water and the air with pollution and ionizing radiation. And last, we prey on the very structure of the earth which provides the vital distribution of that most valuable commodity of all, water. We know that no predatory animal can eliminate its prey without eliminating itself. And yet we have and continue to destroy vast amounts of what we live upon. So far we have been able to move on when we have exhausted an area or make do with some other or new way of extracting a living from the old. So far we in America have not run out. But the awful shadow of running out has fallen on large areas of our earth. In many places — India, China, the Near East, and the like — an ordinary human never once satisfies his hunger, from birth to death, with proper food.

The destruction that men inflict on lands and peoples with machines of war is a matter of the very gravest concern to every sane human, of course. The slow attrition of that other great agent of destruction, misuse of the land, perhaps takes a greater toll in suffering but goes almost unnoticed. During World War II part of our duties included the estimation of bomb damage by studying aerial photographs of bombed cities. Among the most shocking pictures we saw, however, were some high-altitude photographs of unbombed rural China — mile upon mile of bare hills, stripped, eroding, sterile, desolated and left barren by man's misuse. This sort of destruction of life is not limited to the so-called backward countries. Most people are not aware that the bare hills of the West Highlands of Scotland were once healthy northern forests of oak, birch, and pine. This timber was recklessly cut to provide lumber for the British navy and charcoal for early iron smelting. In early times huge areas were simply burned as the easiest way to dislodge outlaw bands or to get the trees out of the way. Later more land was cleared for sheep, which then prevented reforestation through overgrazing. The dynamics of the endless cycle of the materials of life from soil, to plant, to animal, and back to soil again were interrupted. Today the windswept peat bog and bracken-covered acid soil is able to support comparatively few impoverished humans and animals. In the United States our own disastrous dust storms of the thirties and those of more recent years are but one type of evidence of our own misuse of the land. It is true that scientific conservation has done much to solve these problems, but we are still operating in the red with all our resources.

To add to the complexity of this picture of dwindling resources, there is no longer any effective natural control of human numbers aside from the threatened eventuality of sheer starvation or catastrophic war. Some tell us that all this worry is silly. In our country, at any rate, our storage bins are running over. There is possible food for many more billions of humans if we learn to use *all possible* sources. All possible sources include algae from the sea (we are already casting hungry eyes on this source) or the so far uninvented food pill of the future. All sources also include eliminating every other living thing that uses energy or space that we can use ourselves. Actually, this squeeze is on right now. To many it is considered naïve, impractical, or downright un-patriotic to object when some part of the environment — a wild spot, a bit of wetland, a few trees, or perhaps a whole river valley — is wiped out in the name of progress.

But what is progress? Is the destiny of the human species to be uncontrolled expansion until a maximum population on a minimum diet is reached? This is the logical conclusion of the food-pill way of thinking. We are certain that no human being, with the exception of a few narrow specialists, would so define progress. Progress must be toward the richest, fullest life for the greatest number of individuals who can exist on earth within the limits of that good life. Just exactly what a "good" life is is hard to say. It certainly is not an anthill existence where the total human mass is all that matters. No human life can be "good" without the values we call intangibles: beauty, space, self-fulfillment, and the opportunity to be an individual. Because these are the important human characteristics and human needs. These are the qualities that make humans human.

Intangibles brings us back to birds. Various practical reasons are given for protecting birds. They eat harmful insects (beneficial ones too), scavenge carrion, and do a thousand other tasks to preserve or strike a healthy environmental balance. The space and vegetation necessary for their well-being is also necessary for a healthy land. It is encouraging to find that sound agricultural practices are also sound conservation for birds and other wildlife. It is pointed out that preserved wild areas and the animal communities within them are living museums of the past — refuges for natural conditions that might, who knows, produce the antibiotic of the future in their soils or answer some vexing biological problem from a study of their relationships. Perhaps wild places and their inhabitants fill a biological gap that would be dangerous to us if empty. Recreation values are considered "important" for those who like to "get away from it all." Nature study encourages the young to develop their natural interest in biology and helps provide badly needed scientists for the future.

It somehow seems necessary for conservationists to make every consideration a practical one. It is not thought quite valid to preserve anything for esthetic or spiritual reasons. We blush to admit that we might think a bird of value because it is "just beautiful." This leads to what amounts to a leaning over backward to justify the existence of such things as birds and the habitat they need.

With all this emphasis on obvious utility a most important point gets missed. We pay little attention to a realistic evaluation of the utility of intangibles. Can man live by bread alone? Not can he live well or happily — but can he *live at all*, as a man, without these elements of human life he calls intangible? Strange things happen to the minds of men and other animals when they are forced to exist in environments too far removed from those that formed them during the course of their evolution. Many creatures die in captivity for no material reason at all. Many that do not die as individuals cannot reproduce and thus die genetically. In experimental populations of small rodents, overcrowding leads to anxiety and anxiety to an increase in the death rate from "shock" — for lack of a better word. It is now considered quite possible that such adjustments of numbers as the well-known lemming migrations or the cyclic collapse of rabbit populations are brought about by stress.

At what point in the course of this synthetically sustained future will a state of overcrowding take place for man? We know that our emotional and mental qualities are as much evolutionary adaptations as are our physical characteristics. The realization of beauty is one of the most important factors that made man Man. At what point will we be so far removed from the conditions that shaped this evolution of our species that even our amazing mental flexibility breaks down? The human spirit does not burn brightly in crowded slums of cities, or among the apathetic, fatalistic masses of impoverished and overpopulated lands. At what point between the extremes of the first bare subsistence of primitive man and the bare subsistence society of the future lies the optimum? It certainly is not to be found in the romantic Rousseauian dream of natural man, the noble savage. It cannot conceivably exist in the standing-room-only life of the future. Where this point is and how we shall recognize it and maintain it is one of the most serious questions of our time.

As mature human beings our most important job in life may be to assume some of the responsibility for directing progress along truly human lines. In this it seems clear that we need the intangible elements every bit as much as the practical. And if we need a thing to live by it is no longer really intangible, but practical too. Perhaps we should stop referring to beauty and living space as intangibles. Perhaps the preservation of such things as birds and woods and marshes for the sake of their beauty alone is just as important as their destruction is for building a great productive factory. It could be more so.

Suggestions
for Further Reading

Suggestions
for Further Reading

BIRDS

Bent, A. C. *Life Histories* of North American Birds. Published in 20
volumes, 1919–58. Some out-of-print volumes have been reprinted
and are currently available.

Fisher, James. *A History of Birds*. Boston: Houghton Mifflin, 1954.

——. *Watching Birds*. London: Penguin Books, 1951.

——, and Lockley, R. M. *Sea-Birds*. Boston: Houghton Mifflin, 1954.

Kortright, Francis H. *The Ducks, Geese and Swans of North America*.
Harrisburg, Pa.: Stackpole and Wildlife Management Institute,
Washington, D.C., 1953.

Murphy, Robert C. *Oceanic Birds of South America*. New York: American Museum of Natural History, 1936.

Pettingill, Olin S. *A Laboratory and Field Manual of Ornithology*. Min-
neapolis: Burgess, 1956.

Van Tyne, Josselyn, and Berger, Andrew J. *Fundamentals of Ornithology*. New York: Wiley, 1959.

Wallace, George J. *An Introduction to Ornithology*. New York: Mac-
millan, 1955.

Wolfson, Albert, ed. *Recent Studies in Avian Biology*. Urbana: University of Illinois Press, 1955.

IDENTIFICATION

Peterson, Roger Tory. *A Field Guide to the Birds* (2nd rev. ed., 1947) and *A Field Guide to Western Birds* (rev. ed., 1961). Boston: Houghton Mifflin.

Pough, Richard H. *Audubon Land Bird Guide* (1946), *Audubon Water Bird Guide* (1951), and *Audubon Western Bird Guide* (1957). Garden City, N.Y.: Doubleday.

Saunders, Aretas A. *A Guide to Bird Songs*. Garden City, N.Y.: Doubleday, 1951.

MIGRATION

Dorst, Jean. *The Migrations of Birds*. Tr. by Constance D. Sherman. Boston: Houghton Mifflin, 1962.

Lincoln, Frederick C. *The Migration of Birds*. Garden City, N.Y.: Doubleday, 1952.

Matthews, G. V. T. *Bird Navigation*. Cambridge: Cambridge University Press, 1955.

FLIGHT

Aymar, Gordon. *Bird Flight*. Garden City, N.Y.: Garden City Publishing Co., 1938.

Jameson, William. *The Wandering Albatross*. New York: Morrow, 1959.

Queeny, Edgar M. *Prairie Wings*. New York: Lippincott, 1947.

Storer, John H. *The Flight of Birds*. Bloomfield Hills, Mich.: Cranbrook Institute of Science, 1948.

BEHAVIOR

Allee, Warder C. *The Social Life of Animals*. Rev. ed. Boston: Beacon Press, 1958.

Armstrong, Edward A. *Bird Display and Behaviour*. London: Drummond, 1947.

Lack, David. *The Life of the Robin*. Rev. ed. London: Penguin Books, 1953.

Lorenz, Konrad. *King Solomon's Ring*. New York: Crowell, 1952.

Thorpe, William H. *Learning and Instinct in Animals*. Cambridge: Harvard University Press, 1956.

Tinbergen, Niko. *Curious Naturalists*. London: Country Life, 1958.

——. *The Herring Gull's World*. London: Collins, 1953.

——. *The Study of Instinct*. London: Oxford University Press, 1951.

GENERAL BIOLOGY

Buchsbaum, Ralph. *Animals without Backbones*. Rev. ed. Chicago: University of Chicago Press, 1948.

Darling, Lois and Louis. *The Science of Life*. New York: World, 1961.

Romer, Alfred S. *The Vertebrate Body*. 2nd ed. Philadelphia: Saunders, 1955.

Simpson, G. G., Pittendrigh, C. S., and Tiffany, L. H. *Life: An Introduction to Biology*. New York: Harcourt Brace, 1957.

Storer, Tracy I. *General Zoology*. 2nd ed. New York: McGraw-Hill, 1951.

Walls, Gordon L. *The Vertebrate Eye and Its Adaptive Radiation*. Bloomfield Hills, Mich.: Cranbrook Institute of Science, 1942.

Wilson, Carl L., and Loomis, Walter E. *Botany*. Rev. ed. New York: A Holt-Dryden Book, 1957.

Young, J. Z. *The Life of Vertebrates*. Oxford: Clarendon Press, 1950.

ECOLOGY AND CONSERVATION

Allee, Warder C., and Others. *Principles of Animal Ecology*. Philadelphia: Saunders, 1949.

Allen, Durward L. *Our Wildlife Legacy*. New York: Funk & Wagnalls, 1954.

Bates, Marston. *The Forest and the Sea*. New York: Random House, 1960.

Darling, F. Fraser. *Natural History in the Highlands and Islands*. London: Collins, 1947.

Odum, Eugene P. *Fundamentals of Ecology*. Philadelphia: Saunders, 1953.

Osborn, Fairfield. *Our Plundered Planet*. Boston: Little, Brown, 1948.

Storer, John H. *The Web of Life*. New York: Devin-Adair, 1953.

Thomas, William L., Jr., ed. *Man's Role in Changing the Face of the Earth*. Published for Wenner-Gren Foundation for Anthropological Research and National Science Foundation by the University of Chicago Press, 1956.

EVOLUTION, SYSTEMATICS, AND GENETICS

Colbert, Edwin. *Evolution of the Vertebrates*. New York: Wiley, 1955.

Darwin, Charles R. *The Origin of Species*. New York: Modern Library, 1948.

——. *The Voyage of the Beagle*. London: Dent, 1950.

Dobzhansky, Theodosius. *Evolution, Genetics, and Man*. New York: Wiley, 1955.

Dunn, Leslie C., and Dobzhansky, T. *Heredity, Race, and Society*. Rev. ed. New York: New American Library, 1952.

Lack, David. *Darwin's Finches*. Cambridge: Cambridge University Press, 1947.

Mayr, Ernst, and Amadon, Dean. "A Classification of Recent Birds," *American Museum Novitates*, No. 1496 (1953).

Moore, Raymond C. *Introduction to Historical Geology*. New York: McGraw-Hill, 1949.

Romer, Alfred S. *Man and the Vertebrates*. 3rd ed. Chicago: University of Chicago Press, 1941.

Simpson, George G. *Life of the Past: An Introduction to Paleontology*. New Haven: Yale University Press, 1953.

Wetmore, Alexander. *A Revised Classification for Birds of the World* in *Smithsonian Miscellaneous Collections*, Vol. 177, No. 4 (1951).

GENERAL

Berrill, N. J. *Man's Emerging Mind*. New York: Dodd, Mead, 1955.

Eiseley, Loren. *The Firmament of Time*. New York: Atheneum Press, 1960.

——. *The Immense Journey*. New York: Random House, 1957.

Huxley, Julian. *Evolution in Action*. New York: Harper, 1953.

Simpson, George G. *The Meaning of Evolution*. New Haven: Yale University Press, 1950.

Biological supplies, specimens, materials, and equipment can be obtained from the General Biological Supply House, 761–63 East 69th Place, Chicago, Illinois. This remarkable firm can supply anything from a culture of amoebas to a whale embryo, from a butterfly net to a microscope.

Index

Index

ILLUSTRATIONS are placed close to text references throughout the book. Only those separated from the text are listed below.

Adaptation, 35–37, 41, 48–49, 50, 151, 225
Adaptive radiation, 37
Adrenal glands, 193
Aepyornithiformes, 19
Air sacs, 167, 175–77
Albatrosses, 20
  display, 60
  flight, 233–34
  flight speed, 233
  soaring, 230–31
  wings, 223, 232–33
Amphibia, 7, 10
Analogous, 154
Anas, 20
Animalia, 6
Anseriformes, 19
Apteria, 119
Aquilavus, 19
Arbacia, eggs and sperm of, 86–87
Archaeopteryx, xi, 13–17, 19, 21, 29, 153

lithographica, 13
Archaeornis siemensi, 13
Arthropoda, 6, 9
Aves, 7
Aythya, 20

Banding birds, 96
Barton, Roger, ix
Bats, keels in, 142
  migration, 101
Bavaria, fossil bird discovered in, 13
Beaks, 125–27
  skeleton of, 128–31
Beebe, William, 168
Behavior, xii, 46–49
  social, xii, 86–93
  See also Instinct, Display, Learning, Migration *and* Reproductive cycle
Bill. *See* Beaks
Billing, 76

Bird watchers, ix–x, 21
Bitterns, eye placement in, 211
Brain, 188–89
Brant, adaptive specialization in, 39–40
Breathing. *See* Respiratory system
Brood spots, 119
Broodiness, 78, 79, 192
Bubo, predecessor of, 20
Buteo buteo, visual acuity, 207

Caeca, 159
Cambrian period, 4, 8–9
Carboniferous period, 4, 10
Cave drawings, 21
Cedar waxwing, learning in, 68
Cenozoic era, 4, 5
Charadriiformes, 20
Chickens
    ancestors, 19
    broodiness in, 79
    courtship feeding in, 76
    eyes, 212 (*illus.* 215)
    imprinting, 69
    learning, 64
    Leghorn, broodiness in, 70
    muscles, 142
    "peck order," 87–89, 90
    repulsing of young, 84
    skull bones, 128–33
Chordata, 7
Chromosomes, 27, 28
Ciconiiformes, 19
Circulatory system, 162–66
Class, 7
Classification, 5–8
Cloaca, 159, 181–83
Coition, 76–77, 183
Colonial nesters, 92
Color, 120

and communication, 121–22
conspicuous and inconspicuous, 58–59, 118
cryptic, 120–21
eye filters, 205–6
of grebe's feet, 151–52
Conditioning, 68
Condors, wings and soaring in, 226, 232–33
Conservation, 240–42. *See also* Ecology
Cooperation, social, 26, 87, 89–93
Coots, take-off, 226
Correns, Karl, 26
Courtship rituals, 59–60, 62, 63, 74–76, 78. *See also* Display
Cranes, 20
    sandhill, display, 59
    whooping, threat of extinction in, 40, 92; trachea in, 173
Cretaceous period, 4
    birds of, 17–19, 21
Crop, 157–58
Cryptic coloration, 120–21
Cuckoo, European, behavior in, 81–82

Dances, communal, 59
Darwin, Charles, 8, 13, 34
    theory of evolution, 24–26
"Derived activity," 63
Devonian period, 4, 10
Diatryma, 20
Digestive system, 156–60
Dinosaurs, birdlike, 16
Diomedea exulans, 234
Diomedeidae, 20
Disease, 39
Displacement activity, 60–63
Display, 52–54, 74–76, 78

Down feathers, 114–15, 116, 117
Ducks
  ancestors, 19
  bills, 127
  courtship preening, 63
  diving, 20
  imprinting, 69–73
  molting, 118
  plumage, 58
  reaction to danger, 66
  surface, 20, 58
  take-off, 226
  See also Mallards *and* Teal

Eagles, 19, 20 (*illus.* 50)
  eyes, 209, 213
Ears, 128, 195–201
Echinodermata, 6
Eclipse plumage, 118
Ecology, 47, 237–43
Eelgrass, 40
Egg, amniote, development of, 10,
  35
  in ovary, 181
Egg laying, 78–79
Elephant-birds, 19
Emotion, 47–49
Endocrine glands, 99, 190–94
Enemy identification in jackdaws,
  90
Environment, 37–40, 237–38. *See
  also* Ecology
Eocene epoch, birds of, 4, 19–20,
  21
Epidemic disease, 39
Equilibrium, structures of, 195–98
Eras, 5
Esophagus, 157, 169
Evolution, 8, 23–42
Extinction, 37–41

Eyes
  accommodation, 204–5
  acuity, 205–9
  cells, 203–4, 205–8
  lids, 214–15
  pecten, 215–16
  placement, 209–11
  sensitivity, 205–8
  shape, 211–14
  size, 202–3, 213–14
  structure, 132, 203–9, 211–12

Falconiformes, 19
Family, 7
Feathers, 15, 111–19
  color, 120–21
  contour, 114, 116–17, 118–19
  down, 114–15, 116, 117
  flight, 111–14, 118, 144–45, 219,
    221–22, 224, 233
  growth of, 116–17
  hair (filoplume), 115
  molting, 117–18
  of alula, 144, 221, 233
  replacement of, 118
  semiplumes, 115
  shape, 218, 222–23, 226, 232–
    33
  structure of, 111–13
  tracts, 119
Feeding, 80, 81–82, 84
  courtship, 75–76
  See also Digestive system *and* Food
    requirements
Feet
  adaptations in, 41, 148, 150–52
  skeleton of, 147, 151
Filoplumes, 115
Finches, Darwin's, 32–34
Fishes, 4, 7, 10, 212

Flamingo, 20 (*illus.* 23)
  color, 120
Flickers
  display, 59–60
  egg laying in, 78
  tongue, 134
Flight, xii, 217–25
  formations, 91
  hovering, 227–28
  soaring, 228–34
  speed, 235
  take-off and landing, 226–27
  vertical, 227
  See also Wings
Flocks, social organization of, 87–93
Flyways, 96–97
Fog, traveling in, 102–3
Food, human, possible sources, 240
Food requirements, birds', 95, 160–61
Fossil records, 8–9
  of birds, 13–20, 23, 29, 153
Fovea, 208–11
Fowl, domestic. *See* Chickens
Fusion, bone, 15, 16, 147, 152–53

Galápagos Islands, 32–34
Galliformes, 19
Gametes, 27
Gannets (*illus.* 86)
  display, 59
  take-off, 226
Gaping, 80–82
Geese
  ancestors, 19
  Canada (*illus.* 74), 94, 103
  flight formation, 91
  graylag, 69
  imprinting, 69
  molting, 118

  reaction to danger, 66
  take-off, 226
Genes, 27–30
Genetic
  drift, 40–41
  isolation, 31–34
  selection and survival, 30
Genetics, 27–29. *See also* Heredity
Genus, 7, 31
Geospiza, 32
Gizzard, 158–59
Glands
  adrenal, 193
  endocrine, 99, 190–94
  oil and skin, 122
  pancreatic, 194
  parathyroid, 193
  pituitary, 79, 99, 100, 131, 191–93
  salivary, 156–57
  thymus, 194
  thyroid, 99, 193
Gliding. *See* Soaring
Grebes, 20
  feet, 151–52
  great crested, courtship, 60
Gregory, Joseph T., 18
Grosbeak, rose-breasted, beak of, 131
Grouse, ruffed
  copulation, 76
  cycles, 39
Gruiformes, 20
Gulls, 20
  attacks on predators, 91
  brood spots, 119
  egg laying in, 78
  herring: bill color, 82–84, 120; egg laying in, 78; eyes, 208; skeleton of, *illus.* 123
  soaring flight, 231–32

Gulls *(cont'd)*
  territory, 93
  Tinbergen's experiments with, 82–84

Hatching, 80, 81, 82
Hawks, 19, 20
  eyes, 202, 207, 209, 213
  flight speed, 235
Hearing, 198–201
Heart, 163, 164–66
Heath hen, genetic drift in, 40
Heredity, 23–42
  mechanics of, 27–29
  See also Genetics
Heron, great blue
  beak, 127
  flight speed, 235
  leg, 148
Hesperornis, 17–18, 19, 21, 38
Hesperornithidae, 17
Hess, E. H., 69–70
Homologous, 154
Hormones, 99, 190–94
Hovering, 227–28
Hummingbirds
  breathing in, 178
  hovering in, 228
  metabolic rate, 166
Huxley, Sir Julian, 60
Huxley, Thomas, 13

Ichthyornis, 17, 18, 19, 21
Imprinting, 69–73
Insight, 69
Instinct, 46–56
Intangibles, assessment of, 241–43
Intestines, 159, 160
Invertebrates, 9

Jackdaw, 89–90

Journal of Researches (Darwin), 34
Junco, slate-colored, migration experiments with, 98
Jurassic period, 4, 11, 29

Kansas, bird fossils found in, 17
Kidneys, 179–81
Kingdom, 5–6
Kingfishers, eyes of, 206, 209
Kiwi, eyes of, 207
Kramer, Gustav, 104

Lack, David, 52, 53, 56, 65, 74
Land, misuse of, 238–41
"Language," bird, 62–63
Larynx, 168, 169
"Law of effort," 70
Learning, 64–73
  ability, 188–89
Leg
  grebe, 151
  owl, 150
  skeleton (*illus.* 136), 147–48
Leg bands, 96
Leghorn chickens, brooding in, 70
Limpkin, 20
Linnaean system of classification, 5–8
Linnaeus, 5, 8
Liver, 159, 179
Lorenz, Konrad, 69, 82, 88, 89
Lungs, 173–77
Lymphatic system, 163

Mallards
  bills, 127
  flight speed, 235
  imprinting, 69–70, 71–73
  syrinx, 172
  vertical flight, 227

Mammalia, 7
Man, coming of, 4, 21
Marsh, Othniel C., 13, 17, 18
Mayr, Ernst, ix
Meiosis, 27
Mendel, Gregor Johann, 26–27, 46
Metabolism, 155–56, 159–60, 165–66, 177
Migration, xii, 94–95
  banding, 96
  basic cause for, 95–96
  distances covered, 97–98, 103
  effect of light on, 98, 100, 101
  environmental and psychological stimuli, 99–101
  flyways, 96–97
  navigation during, 102–8
  physiological reasons for, 99–100
  rates of speed, 97, 103
  "whys" of, 98–101
Miocene epoch, 4, 20, 21
Mollusca, 6
Molting, 117–18
Mouths, 156, 157
  nestlings', 80–81
Murphy, Robert Cushman, 234
Muscles, 125
  flight, 142–43, 144–45
  gizzard, 158–59
  heart, 152
  leg, 148
  smooth, 152
  striated, 152
Mutations, 28–29, 31

Natural selection, 25. *See also* Evolution
Navigation, 102–8
Nervous system, 184–89, 190, 191
Nest building, 50, 51, 77–78

Nestlings, caring for, 80–82, 84, 160–61
Nictitans, 214–15
Nightingales, song, 65

Odontognathae, 18
Oil gland, 122
Oligocene epoch, 4, 20
Order, 7
Ordovician period, 4, 9
Origin of Species (Darwin), 8, 13, 24, 26, 34
Ostrich, 19
  eyes, 202, 208, 215
  loss of keel, 142
Ovary, 181, 183, 193
Owen, Sir Richard, 13
Owls, 20
  ears and hearing, 200, 201
  eyes, 202, 207–8, 212, 213–14
  great horned: beak, 131; talons, 148–50

Pancreas, 159, 194
Pancreatic glands, 194
Parathyroid glands, 193
Passeriformes, 7, 20
"Peck order," 87–89, 93
Pecten, 215–16
Peepers, spring, 168–69
Pelecaniformes, 19
Pelvis, 145–46, 148
Penguins
  behavior, 59, 78, 93
  cryptic coloration, 121
  emperor, breeding of, 100
  feeding captive, 52
  fossils, 20
  keel, 142
  skeleton, 153

Penguins *(cont'd)*
  wing bones, 124
Phasianus, 20
Pheasants, 12, 20
  wing shape and flight, 223
Photosynthesis, 9
Phylum, 6–7
Pigeons
  breathing, rate of, 178
  broodiness in, 79
  courtship feeding, 76
  crop, 157
  display, 60
  ears, 195, 198
  eyes, 206
  heart, 166
  homing, 102
  muscles, 139–43 (*illus.* 149)
  skeleton, 135–39, 143–44, 145–
    47, 153; compared with *Ar-
    chaeopteryx, illus.* 15, 153
  syrinx, 171–72
  wing aspect ratio, 233
"Pigeon's milk," 157, 192
Pigments, 120
Pisces, 7
Pituitary gland, 79, 99, 100, 131,
  191–93
Plantae, 6
Plants, xvii, 4, 5, 9, 35, 156
Pleistocene epoch, 4, 20–21
Pliocene epoch, 4, 20–21
Plovers, migration of, 97–98
Populations, 24, 29–32
Porifera, 6
Prairie Wings (Queeny), 227
Pre-Cambrian era, 4, 9
Preening, 60, 62, 63, 113
Pre-herons, 19
Pre-pelicans, 19

Pre-vultures, 19
Progress, 241
Prolactin, 79, 192
Protective coloration, 120–21
Protista, 5
Pseudosuchia, 16
Pterodactyls, keels in, 142
Pterosaurs, 16
Pterylosis, 119
Puffinus, 20

Quails, learning in, 66–67
Queeny, Edgar, 227

Rails, 20
Recent epoch, 4, 20–21
Rectrices, 114, 118
Remiges, 114, 118, 144
Reproductive cycle, 74–85
Reproductive system, 181–83
Reptiles, 4, 32, 166
  birds evolved from, 11, 15, 16,
    153
  ears, 199
  evolution, 10, 13, 35, 154
  eyes, 205, 212, 214, 215
  flying, 16, 142
  swimming, 18
Reptilia, 7
Respiratory system, 167–78
"Ritualization," 60
Robins
  American, 7; head-cocking, 210
  European, behavior, 52, 53–56,
    65, 74
Rowan, William, 98

Salivary glands, 156–57
Sandpipers, 20
  flight speed, 235

Sauer, E. G. Franz, 105

Schweitzer, Albert, 237

Sciences, xi, 45–46, 237

Scotland, deforestation of, 240

Sea urchin, eggs and sperm of, 86

Semiplumes, 115

. Sex, 27–28. *See also* Heredity *and* Reproductive cycle

Sexual organs, 181–83, 192–93

Shearwater, Manx, migration of, 103, 107

Shrikes, 20

  eyes, 209

Sight, 202–16. *See also* Eyes

Signals, 62–63. *See also* Display

Skeleton, 123–25

  Archaeopteryx, 15–16, 153

  fusion and loss of bones, 152–53

  leg, 147–48, 151

  pectoral girdle, 137–39, 143

  pelvic girdle, 145–46, 148

  ribs, 137, 139

  skull, 127–34. *See also* Beaks

  sternum, 137

  vertebral column, 134–37, 153

  wing, 137, 143–44

Skin, 116, 119, 120, 122

Skull, 127–34

Slotting. *See* Wings

Smell, 207

  kiwi's sense of, 207

Soaring, 228–33

Song, 65, 169, 173. *See also* Syrinx

Sparrows

  eyes, 206–7

  grasshopper, 65

  heartbeat, 166

  house, 119, 206–7

Species, 30–34

  identification of, x, xvi

number of, ix, xi–xii

Origin of, 8, 13, 24–25, 34

Spinal cord, 135, 185

Starlings

  heart, 166

  migration, 104–5

  syrinx, *illus.* 171

Stomach, 158–59

Storks, 19

Strix, 20

Struthioniformes, 19

"Supernormal stimulus," 84

Swallows

  egg laying in, 78

  eyes, 207, 209

  migration, 103

  song, 65

Swans

  ancestors, 19

  body temperature, 166

  mute: cervical vertebrae, 135; heart, 166

  take-off, 226

  trumpeter, threat of extinction in, 40

Swifts

  flight speed, 235

  temperature of, 166

Syrinx, 171–73

Systema Naturae (Linnaeus), 5

Teal, blue-winged, migration of, 97

Teeth, 16, 18–19, 128, 153

Temperature, body, 160, 165–66, 167, 177

Terns, migration of, 95, 103

Territorial behavior, 52–54, 61, 74, 92–93

Tertiary period, 4, 19

Testes, 181, 183, 192
Thymus gland, 194
Thyroid gland, 193
Tinbergen, Niko, 63, 82, 83, 84
Tongue, 133–34, 157
Trachea, 169, 172–73
Trial-and-error learning, 68
Tschermak, Eric von, 26
Turdidae, 7
Turdus, 7

Urinary system, 179–81

Vertebrae. *See* Skeleton
Vertebrate Eye, The (Walls), 209
Vertebrates, 4, 7, 11
Vocal organs, 168–73. *See also* Syrinx
Voyage of the Beagle, The (Darwin), 34
Vries, Hugo de, 26
Vultures, 20
    thermal soaring, 228–29

Wagtails, 20
Walls, Gordon, 209
Warblers, 20

migration experiments with, 105–7
Weather migrants, 95–96
Weaverbird nests, 77
Webbed feet, 41, 151
Whales, ix
    skeleton, 123–24
Whip-poor-will, eyes of, 207
Whitethroat, lesser, migration experiments with, 105
Wings, xii
    muscles of, 142–43, 144–45
    propeller action, 223–25, 227–28
    shape, 218–23, 226, 232–33
    skeleton of, 143–44
    slotting, 221–22, 233–34
    See also Flight
Wishbone, 139, 169
Woodcocks, eye placement in, 211
Woodpeckers, 20
    feet, 150–51
    See also Flickers

Yellowlegs, lesser, flight speed of, 97

Zoological nomenclature, 8